Leeds College of Building   Leeds

Solar Heating Design and Installation Guide

2007

© August 2007

The Association of Plumbing and Heating Contractors, the Chartered Institution of Building Services Engineers, the Council for Registered Gas Installers, the Heating & Hotwater Industry Council, the Heating and Ventilating Contractor's Association, the Institute of Domestic Heating & Environmental Engineers, the Institute of Plumbing and Heating Engineering, the Oil Firing Technical Association, the Scottish and Northern Ireland Plumbing Employers Federation, the Underfloor Heating Manufacturers Association.

ISBN 978-1-903287-84-2

Cover design by Tattersall Hammarling & Silk

Typesetting & layout by Free Thinking Design

Printed in Malta by Print Solutions Partnership

Contents

Organisations making up the Domestic Building Services Panel of The Chartered Institution of Building Services Engineers

Association of Plumbing and Heating Contractors	**APHC**
Chartered Institution of Building Services Engineers	**CIBSE**
Council for Registered Gas Installers	**CORGI**
Electrical Contractors' Association	**ECA**
Heating and Hotwater Industry Council	**HHIC**
Heating and Ventilating Contractors' Association	**HVCA**
Institute of Domestic Heating and Environmental Engineers	**IDHEE**
Institute of Plumbing and Heating Engineering	**IPHE**
Manufacturers of Domestic Unvented Systems	**MODUS**
National Inspection Council for Electrical Installation Contracting	**NICEIC**
Oil Firing Technical Association	**OFTEC**
The Scottish and Northern Ireland Plumbing Employers Federation	**SNIPEF**
The Underfloor Heating Manufacturers Association	**UHMA**
The UK Government's Energy Efficiency Best Practice in Housing	**EEBPH**

Copies of this Guide are available from the bodies whose contact details are given in Appendix G.

Foreword

National requirements for energy conservation have resulted in the need to significantly expand the installation of solar thermal heating systems, so as to reduce the amount of fossil fuel used to generate heat. However, a considerable gap exists between the growing demand for competent design and installation work in this field and the available capacity to meet that demand in a professional manner in both the UK and Ireland.

This gap has resulted in the installation of many unsatisfactory solar thermal heating systems, particularly where heating domestic hot water.

To provide guidance to those designing and installing solar heating systems and to support training and certification schemes, the Domestic Building Services Panel of CIBSE has drawn up this Guide to cover the design and installation of solar domestic water heating. The Guide covers the predominant types of such systems and notes their advantages and disadvantages. The broad range of systems covered will assist those engaged in repair and maintenance work to understand the principles of operation of a great deal of the equipment that has been installed to date.

The Guide is intended to be read in conjunction with the Domestic Heating Design Guide, first published by the Panel in 2000 and reprinted and updated a number of times since, which covers the main elements of domestic heating system design.

The Panel acknowledges the contribution made to this Guide by Chris Laughton, its technical author and also by other Working Group members. Thanks are particularly due to the late George Henderson who played a notable role in the development of this publication.

The Working Group of the Domestic Building Services Panel responsible for the Guide consisted of the following persons.

Colin Sutherland (Chairman)	Chartered Institution of Building Services Engineers
John Beer	Heating and Hotwater Industry Council
Ian Beard, Alan Keating and Mike Staton	Heating and Ventilating Contractors Association
Chris Laughton (Technical Author)	Institute of Domestic Heating and Environmental Engineers
Robin Oakley	Institute of Plumbing and Heating Engineering

Significant and much valued input was also made by David Lush and Hywel Davies of CIBSE.

Note from the publisher

This publication is primarily intended to provide guidance for those responsible for the design, installation, commissioning, operation and maintenance of building services. It is not intended to be exhaustive or definitive and it will be necessary for users to exercise their own professional judgement when deciding whether to abide or depart from it.

1. Introduction

1.1 Objective

This solar thermal design guide has been produced to assist professional heating engineers to specify and design hot water heating systems that incorporate heat principally derived from the sun.

This is intended to be read in conjunction with other publications in the series produced by the CIBSE Domestic Building Services Panel. Reference must also always be made to the statutory requirements, directives, standards, industry code of practice and energy efficiency guides.

The information is particularly applicable to the UK and Ireland but is generally useful for other locations.

1.2 Scope

Solar thermal is a general term to cover heating processes initiated from the sun's radiation striking building surfaces. It is part of a family of processes and can itself be usefully subdivided into smaller groups, see Figure 1.1.

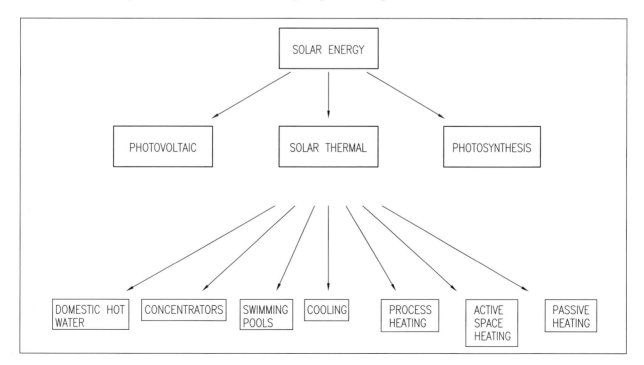

Figure 1.1 The different processes of solar energy

This guide focuses on only one of the sub-groups of solar thermal heating:

- **Solar domestic hot water (Solar DHW)**

This guidance is not limited by the size of the solar heating system, but additional considerations need to be made for large installations. Always check with the equipment manufacturers for suitability.

The guide provides engineering data for solar DHW system design for practitioners who wish to understand and design such systems. It provides a method for agreeing a specification with clients.

The guide may be used to validate training courses in solar DHW system design and in the craft skills required for installation.

1.2   Context

Solar thermal is a renewable energy technology that uses energy sources not depleted by extraction. Renewable energy can help displace the use of more traditional fuels which have diminishing reserves. In doing so, they can also mitigate emissions such as carbon dioxide which contributes to global warming.

2.   Overview

2.1   System terminology

The movement of heat in a solar DHW system can be thought of in two parts:

● A primary heat movement system that collects solar energy and transfers it to a store

● A secondary heat movement system that stores pre-heated water, then treats this water to make it suitable for distribution as DHW for household use

It is useful to compare the movement of fluid through the different parts of the system, as are there are often exchanges of heat but not necessarily fluids. For example, sometimes fluid moves in a closed circuit as shown in Figure 2.1.

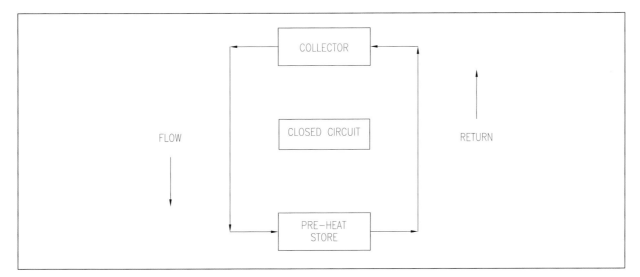

Figure 2.1 The principles of a closed circuit

A closed circuit can be contrasted with water that is ultimately consumed at appliances or terminal devices and hence moves through an open-ended system as shown in Figure 2.2.

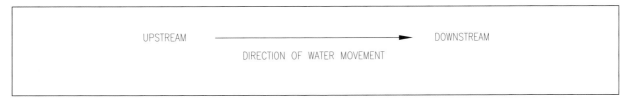

Figure 2.2 The principles of an open ended system

A solar DHW installation operates by moving heat through a combination of closed and open systems to form a complete functional system. Heat movement is not always the same as fluid movement: a heat exchanger may be present, which separates the heat transfer fluid passing through the solar collector from that which is stored and used in the DHW system. It should be noted that, unlike other more conventional heat sources, solar heat is a variable both in quantity and time according to the weather. Due to the levels of solar irradiation in the UK, solar DHW is normally integrated with other heat sources before it becomes useful. It is also extensively stored before use and is not normally considered an instantaneous heat source. The principle of a solar pre-heating system is shown in Figure 2.3.

A solar DHW primary system requires:

- A solar energy collector
- An interconnecting circuit formed with pipes
- A transmission or heat transfer fluid
- A heat exchanger or store.

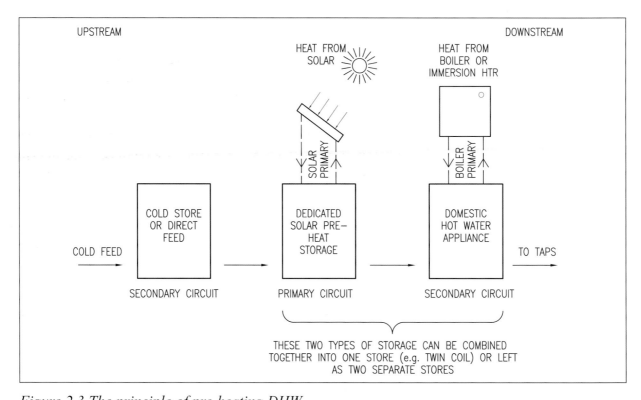

Figure 2.3 The principle of pre-heating DHW

A solar DHW secondary system refers to components holding the water that is intended to be consumed and hence forms an open ended sequence, as shown in Figure 2.4, and includes:

- A cold feed
- An intermediate warm store
- A final hot store or appliance
- A discharge point

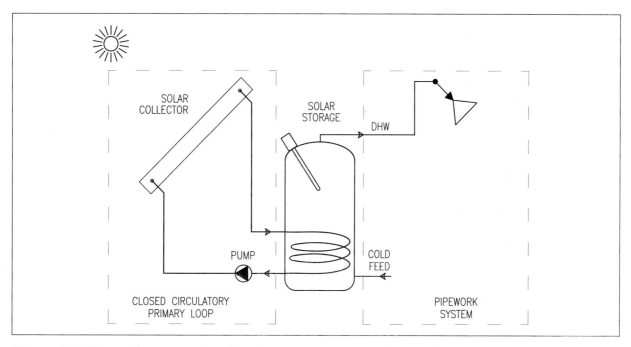

Figure 2.4 The combination of a closed primary circuit and secondary open discharge pipework

Where the primary circuit fluid is different to that of the secondary side of the system, the system can be considered indirect. This would indicate the presence of a heat exchanger in the storage vessel, such as an internal coil or an external plate heat exchanger, as shown in Figure 2.5. This contrasts to systems where the primary transmission fluid and the consumed water are the same; and in these cases the solar DHW system is termed as being of the direct type. Sometimes an indirect system can have more than one heat exchanger, using an intermediary or tertiary arrangement such as with a thermal store.

2.2   The pre-heating of domestic hot water

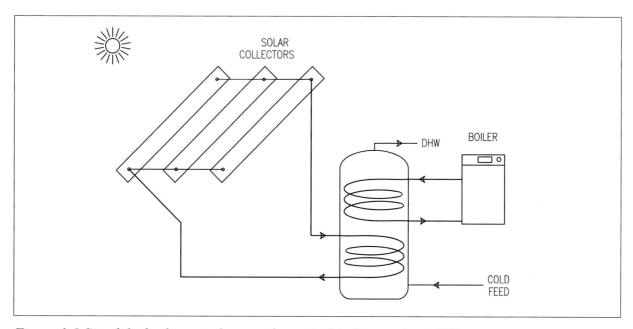

Figure 2.5 Simplified schematic layout of a typical indirect solar DHW system

Where DHW is traditionally heated, such as by an electric immersion heater or an indirect coil from a boiler, the cold feed to the secondary circuit should originate from a wholesome source normally expected to be at a temperature of less than 20°C. This feed water is then raised in temperature by the solar heating system in one phase up to a target temperature of 60°C, it is then stored at no less than 60°C for distribution at no less than 55°C. To control the risk of scalding, a thermostatic blending valve can be fitted at each point of use. These temperature levels are confirmed in WRAS/DEFRA Water Regulations Guide, CIBSE TM13 and BRE IP 14/03.

By introducing solar heat, an intermediate pre-heating stage or warm store is provided where the water is stored at a variable temperature value according to the variable energy supply that comes from the sun. Depending on the amount of solar input available, this temperature can vary not only by day but also by season and can range from the cold feed temperature upwards to steam temperature. Solar energy is an uncontrolled energy source at the point where it enters a collection system and as such must be handled with caution. Pre-heated water from a solar system can at times create conditions ideal for growth of legionella, or at other times can produce scalding water or even high pressure steam. Pre-heated water must not therefore be considered as domestic hot water for distribution until either fully heated by a back-up heat source or temperature controlled to prevent scalding, such as by the use of thermostatic blending valves. A suitably qualified person or heating engineer experienced in the field should oversee the design of hot water services involving solar heat input.

2.3   Heat circulation

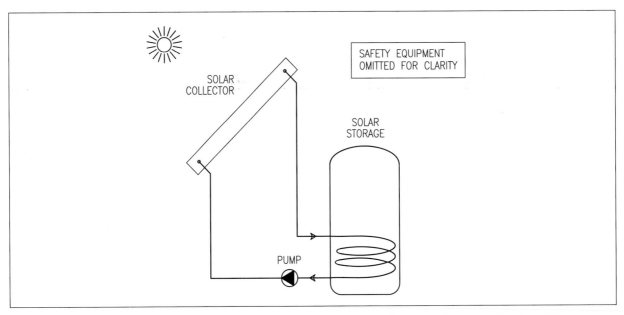

Figure 2.6 Simplified schematic of typical pipework of an indirect and pumped solar DHW

The most common systems for circulating solar heat make use of a pump in the primary system as shown in Figure 2.6, with the following benefits:

- The solar collector can be more easily located upon the roof

- The rate of heat transfer can be controlled

- Small bore pipes can be used

- There are fewer restrictions on the type of solar collector that can be used.

A pump offers the best flexibility and response to intermittent UK weather conditions, it can permit simple protection against overheating and frost damage. The power source of a pump is typically derived from the grid mains electricity and is normally wired through a temperature control, although the power source can also be derived from batteries charged by photovoltaic modules.

The rate of heat transfer (the power of the solar system) can be calculated from the rate of circulation, the heat capacity of the fluid and the temperature difference of the flow and return.

In limited circumstances, it is possible to use natural buoyancy or thermo-siphon to create the circulation instead of a pump as shown in Figure 2.7. This would imply that the heat source, i.e. the collector, is at the lowest point in the circuit with heat rising up to a store. In reality, it is quite difficult to install such systems since the pipes must always rise up from the collector and must not have a bore size of less than 22 mm, although ideally this will be larger.

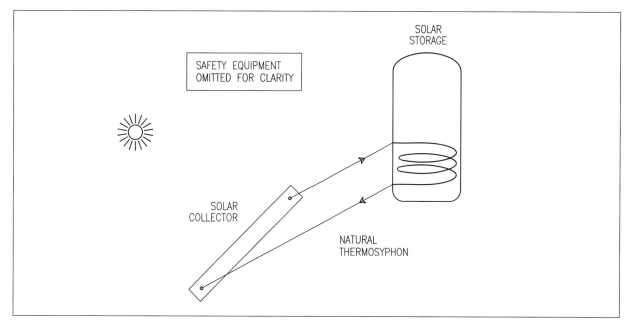

Figure 2.7 Schematic pipework layout of thermo-siphon system

2.4   Primary fluid expansion

As with any heating system, the solar primary fluid will expand when it is heated. Unlike conventional heating systems, the temperature range which causes the expansion is far greater, since the solar collector is mounted externally hence facing the extremes of the climate. Fluid temperatures inside the collector can range from -20°C. to over 130°C. This in turn causes a fluid expansion of around 8%.

However, an even greater expansion occurs in the event that the circulation ceases under strong sunlight conditions. In this case, any liquid in the collector will vaporise, creating a gas that pushes out the remaining liquid that must be accommodated or released. To accommodate this expansion safely, there are three common methods in use:

- A header cistern open to the atmosphere (open vented system)

- An expansion vessel with flexible membrane and safety valve (sealed system)

- A drain-back vessel with an integral air pocket with safety valve or open vent (drain-back system)

3   Systems

3.1   Indirect systems

The predominant form of solar thermal system in the UK and Ireland uses an indirect primary circuit. In these, the heat transfer fluid that passes through the collector is isolated from the consumed water by a form of heat exchanger.

The heat exchanger separates the consumed secondary water from the fluid in the primary collector circuit and hence allows antifreeze and anti-corrosion inhibitors to be added to the latter. This also prevents continual introduction of contaminants from the incoming cold mains from reducing collector efficiency, particularly limescale and sludge. The risk of bacterial growth and scalding is greatly reduced with an indirect circuit, but this must be offset against the loss of efficiency that heat exchange can cause to the solar circuit where the temperature difference between the primary and secondary is increased to permit heat transfer.

The most common heat exchanger is a coil located within the secondary water storage, although external plate exchangers can also be used. The 'mantle' type of exchanger, where the primary fluid passes in a 'jacket' surrounding the hot water cylinder walls is sometimes seen in the UK and Ireland but is common in the rest of Europe.

The sizing of heat exchangers remains critical to maintain collector efficiency since the return temperature of the collector circuit must ideally remain cool to enhance heat transfer in the collector absorber.

Attempts to share the same solar primary circuit with that of the primary circuit of a gas, oil or solid fuel boiler are fraught with difficulties. These include the compatibility of corrosion inhibitors with solar collectors, the protection of freezing and prevention of reverse circulation through a heating appliance that is not hot. It should be especially noted that there is a strong risk that heat generated from a fossil fuel would be circulated at night up to the collector, be emitted and hence lost. A solar primary circuit that is designed to be independent from other indirect circuits and from secondary circuits is the most common method used to avoid such problems.

3.2   Direct systems

Within a direct solar water heating system, the domestic hot water is passed through the solar circuit by circulating it from a domestic hot water store directly through the solar collectors.

Direct solar systems have been fitted in various formats, often connected to a separate pre-heat cylinder or to a combined cylinder with dedicated solar storage volume in the bottom. They may also be found connected to an existing conventional hot water storage vessel with a traditional heat source, e.g. a boiler or an electric immersion heater.

In such circumstances, the solar collector system will normally share the same open safety vent and cold feed with the existing storage cylinder. This means that every water fitting which uses water connected to the mains water supply must use fittings approved by the water supply company. All fittings used must be of an appropriate quality and standard, and be suitable for the circumstances in which they are used. The specific requirements are covered under authoritative guidance from DEFRA and WRAS, as well as the Water Supply (Water Fittings) Regulations 1999. There are also requirements of advance notification to the water provider.

Illustrative schematics for such systems are shown below in Figures 3.1, 3.2 and 3.3.

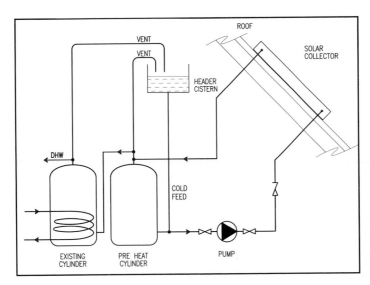

Figure 3.1 Direct solar primary system connected to a separate pre-heat store

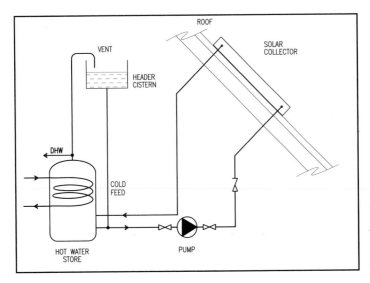

Figure 3.2 Direct solar primary system connected to a combined pre-heat and DHW store

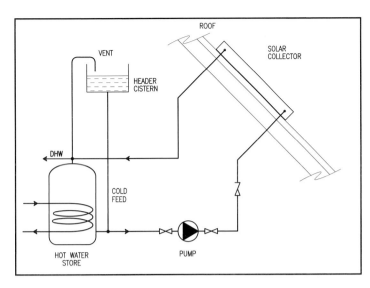

Figure 3.3 Direct solar primary system connected to an existing DHW store with no added dedicated solar storage

There are particular features applicable to direct systems which need to be carefully considered before selecting such systems and they include:

- Scalding risk from possibility of dangerously high water temperatures (or steam) reaching terminal devices during collector stagnation.

- Freezing of fluid in the solar collector and other parts of the primary circuit where it would pose a risk of damage to materials, loss of circulation or blockage of safety vents.

- Greater accumulation of lime-scale, silt and other debris in the solar circuit with loss of circulation, heat transfer, blockage of safety vents or build-up of bacteria.

- Loss of water quality of DHW due to the presence of silt and debris and after contact with materials and fittings during high stagnation temperatures and pressures.

- Backflow or thermo-siphoning of heated water into a cold water cistern containing wholesome water.

- Disturbance of stratification in the solar storage vessel due to pumps, which increase return temperature at the base of the store causing reduced collector efficiency.

- Excess expansion or evaporation of fluids from storage cistern.

Furthermore, there are also particular features applicable to any solar systems connected directly to an existing conventional hot water storage vessel which need to be carefully considered before selecting such systems and they include:

- Loss of dedicated solar storage capacity.

- Loss of the legionella control method from back-up heating appliances.

Further details are given in Chapter 7.

3.3   Open Vented primaries

A solar DHW open vented primary system, as shown in Figure 3.4, has features that distinguish it from conventional open vented heating systems. Firstly, if antifreeze is used, the feed and vent cistern is not normally connected to the cold water mains via a float valve, in case of dilution due to long-term evaporation. Hence, re-filling of the header cistern with antifreeze has to be undertaken manually. Secondly, the cistern needs to be fitted high up in the building to gain the greatest static pressure (head) above the collector. Failure to do this increases the risk of premature boiling within the collector but also may provide insufficient head to enable a circulating pump to operate at high temperatures, resulting in cavitation. It is not always practicable to achieve sufficient height.

A one-way check valve is required whenever a collector is above the store and fully filled with fluid, otherwise at night, when the store can become relatively hotter than the collector, heat would rise from the storage vessel by natural buoyancy and be lost i.e. by gravity circulation. It may be necessary to have such check valves installed in both the flow and return pipes to the collector as unwanted gravity circulation can occur in a single pipe. It should be noted that for safety, the top of the collector is connected as the flow pipe and the vent is connected so that there is no obstruction between it and the collector. This promotes the release of air and is in harmony with the natural buoyancy of solar heated fluid in the collector. A circulation meter is usually fitted in order to monitor and adjust the circulation rate. See further Sections 6.1.1 and 6.1.4.

The issue of pump-over of water from the safety vent pipe is a problem in some configurations, due to the high resistance of the collector to pumped circulation or to

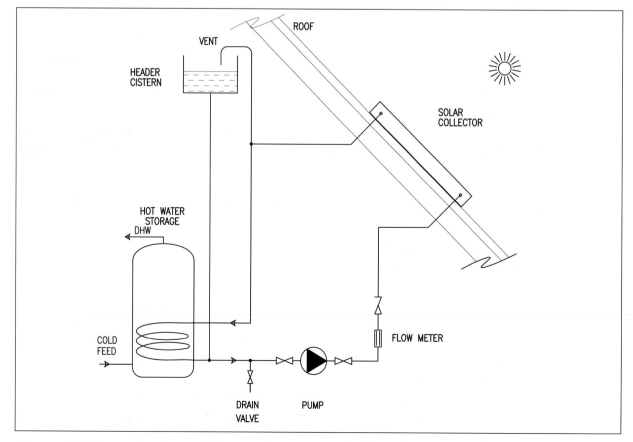

Figure 3.4 Schematic pipework layout of open vented solar primary

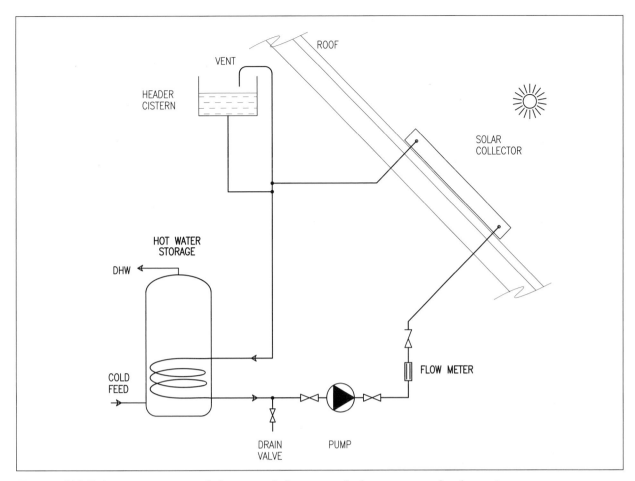

Figure 3.5 Schematic pipework layout of close coupled open vented solar primary

insufficient static head. One solution to this is to use a close-coupled format, placing the cold feed within a short distance after the vent.

The primary system expansion is normally found to be independent of the secondary system, except when the solar DHW system is connected directly to an open vented store. In this case, the open vent of the store serves a dual purpose for both primary and secondary systems. However, this technique is to be approached with caution in the UK for the following reasons:

● The potential for a blockage of the route to safety vents by freezing fluid in the solar collector and other parts of the primary circuit.

● The accumulation of lime-scale, silt or other debris in the primary circuit with gradual loss of circulation, heat transfer or blockage of safety vents.

Solar DHW systems that use indirect open vented primaries, whilst historically interesting, are seldom fitted in recent years due to the problems of evaporation of fluid at high temperatures and premature oxidation of antifreeze fluid. There are also more restrictions on collector and pump locations. The emergence of high performance collectors has also meant that the ease of boiling under low pressure and the limitations of plastic components typically found in cisterns becomes a hindrance. Open vented primary systems are likely to require user intervention during normal operation and hence are unlikely to meet the requirements of Section 4.1.4 of BS EN 12976.

3.4   Fully filled and sealed system primary

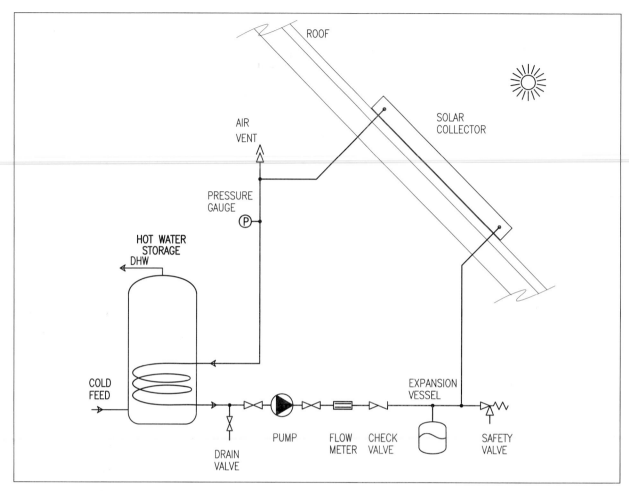

Figure 3.6 Schematic pipework layout of sealed fully filled solar primary

The increased availability of high quality sealed system components for heating installations has made the sealed system the predominant primary layout in the UK and Ireland. Such systems, as shown in Figure 3.6, are also the most suitable type to use with solar heating. At first sight, a sealed, fully-filled solar DHW system appears to share similar components to a conventional sealed heating system namely:

- Expansion vessel
- Spring loaded safety pressure valve
- Pressure gauge
- Air vents
- Filling point which can be combined with drain point

However, it needs to be borne in mind that one consequence of sealing a primary system is that the static pressure is significantly raised above atmospheric by the filling process, typically for solar DHW between 1 and 3 Bar over atmospheric pressure. This in turn raises the boiling point of the primary transmission fluid within the collector making high temperatures above 100°C possible, even in normal operation. The highest temperatures occur when there is a loss of circulation through the solar collector at a time of strong sunlight conditions. When this occurs, fluid temperatures in the collector can exceed 150°C. In solar heating this is known as evaporation which is often quickly followed by stagnation, see also Section 4.1.1, where vapour temperatures can reach over 300°C inside the absorber. This places a far greater strain on the system components from expansion and contraction than would be experienced in a normal heating system, it can melt non-metallic plumbing components such as pipe clips or plastic pipe, see Table 7.17. The location and specification of all components used in a sealed solar primary system thus have to be carefully considered. Solar systems can and should be designed to be 'hydraulically secure' retaining all fluids, even under stagnation conditions when the formation of steam is possible. They can also be designed to restrict the fluid temperatures in order to increase longevity of components.

3.5   Drainback primary

The location of a solar collector normally above the store, allows the possibility of a technique quite special to solar DHW systems, namely the ability to drainback. In this case, the system is only partially filled, leaving an air pocket permanently present in the circulatory circuit. Without the action of a pump, the fluid does not fill the collector but instead rests wholly within the lower part of the circuit. When energised, the pump pushes the air out of the collector replacing it with fluid, the air is then displaced down to inside a 'drainback' vessel, as shown in Figure 3.7.

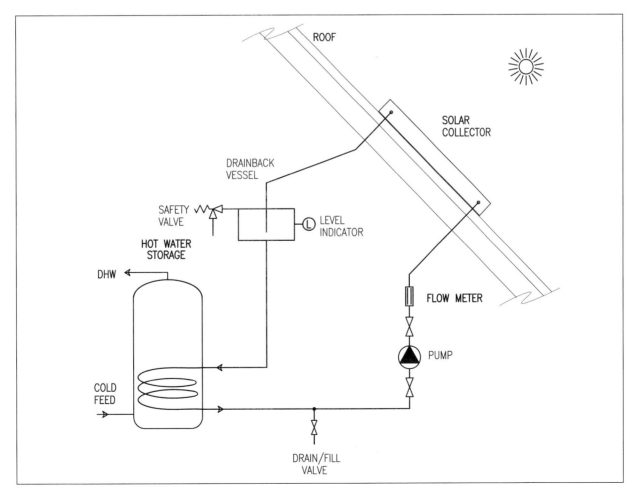

Figure 3.7 Schematic pipework layout of drainback solar primary

The drainback vessel can be located either on the flow or the return pipe of the primary circuit. An open safety vent pipe or more commonly the expansion vessel of a sealed system can provide safety for liquid expansion. Since the default position of the fluid is to drain out of the collector, extremes of expansion can be avoided, although where the pump locks-on during a fault situation, temperatures, above 100°C, can still be achieved. Furthermore, during drainback, the fluid in the collector falls briefly to below atmospheric pressure, occasionally causing premature boiling with accompanying 'kettling' sound. Pipes from the collector must always be run to the drainback vessel with a fall of at least 1:30. Consideration should be given to the acceptability of the extra noise of the air moving through the system. These systems can be designed to be 'hydraulically secure', particularly by using a sealed system and hence retain all fluids even under stagnation conditions. A check valve is not required as normally there would be no liquid left in the in the collector which would otherwise permit unwanted heat loss from the store overnight, see also Section 3.3. Indeed, any such restriction may prevent the drainback from working although consideration should be given to unwanted heat loss by warm air moving upwards in the pipe.

Since it is intended that air is to remain in the circuit, all components containing plain water should be corrosion resistant, although typically the oxygen in the trapped air of a sealed system is quickly lost leaving mainly nitrogen. Whilst the use of antifreeze and/or corrosion inhibitors is possible, their long-term durability may be decreased by the presence of air and high temperatures.

4 Equipment

4.1 Solar collectors

4.1.1 Solar collector terminology

A solar collector generates heat by absorbing solar irradiation and converts this into thermal energy. The part that receives the solar energy is called the absorber. This usually has a translucent cover, which allows light in and reduces heat losses from convection. An insulated enclosure provides structural integrity and reduces losses from conduction. Connectors allow fluid from the primary circuit to circulate from the collector into the dwelling. A solar collector is a generic name covering many types of solar thermal equipment whereas the use of 'solar panels' can lead to confusion with photovoltaic modules.

The collector is mounted on the outside of the building and is therefore subject to extremes of weather. During high irradiation periods, if there is no net heat extraction, an absorber surface will stagnate between 150°C and 300°C. The waterways of the absorber in this state will then contain super-heated fluid or vapour at a pressure of up to 6 bar (six times atmospheric pressure) depending on the safety limiting devices. A collector of good design should be able to survive these conditions safely and reliably, without specialised maintenance, for over 20 years.

4.1.2 Flat plate and tubular collectors

There are two main types of commercially available solar collector for domestic hot water heating; flat plate collectors and tube collectors. These names essentially refer to the shape of the translucent cover but can also mean a tubular absorber.

Although a flat plate collector would particularly appear to be a simple matter to fabricate on site, the extreme conditions that it will be subjected to would normally preclude this and instead there is a large range of ready-made commercial units on the UK market. Furthermore, unless made under factory conditions, it would be difficult to assure the anticipated performance and durability of such a collector. The unwanted ingress of dust, salt, rain, mould and insects can all act to substantially reduce the life of a solar collector. Components used in the construction and fixing of collectors should be selected to survive all the extremes of weather, ultra-violet degradation and rodent attack.

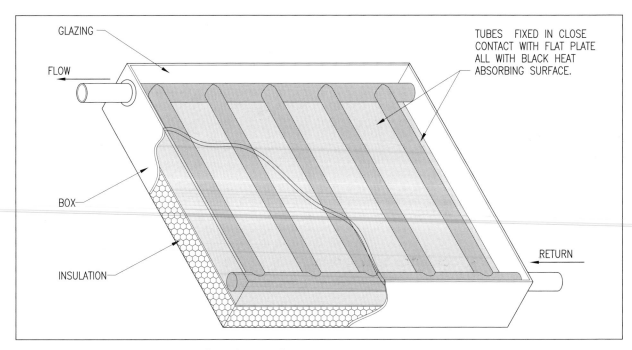

Figure 4.1 Cutaway image of flat plate collector

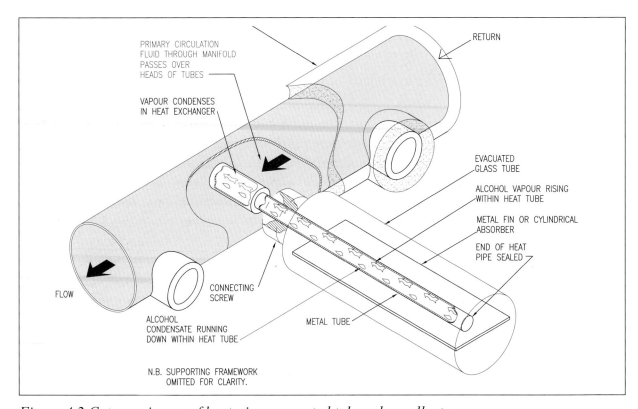

Figure 4.2 Cutaway image of heat-pipe evacuated tube solar collector

Flat plate solar collectors, as shown in Figure 4.1, can be thought of as a 'radiator' in reverse wherby a plate of metal is heated by the direct and indirect solar radiation and fluid is circulated inside the plate. This plate is housed in a box fronted by either glass or plastic and contains either a network of pipes or be compromised of two welded sheets. Special high temperature fabric or foam is used to insulate the sides and rear of the collector.

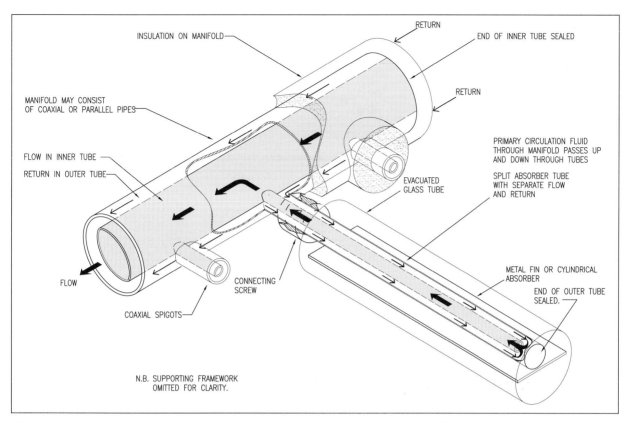

Figure 4.3 Cutaway image of non heat-pipe evacuated tube solar collector

Tubular collectors are frequently sold as glass evacuated tubes which plug into a manifold located at the sides or the top/bottom. The evacuation serves as an insulator against unwanted convected air currents. The tubes can often rotate in the manifold to improve the orientation of the internal absorbers. The primary circulating fluid passes through the manifold and over the heads of the tubes. Some tube designs, called 'heat-pipes', use a separate indirect, alcohol-filled pipe inside each tube to absorb the heat, see Figure 4.2. The heat pipe reduces the risk of contamination or blockage from the primary fluid that may otherwise occur inside the absorber. This also reduces the overall volume of the system hence less expansion occurs and a smaller expansion vessel is required, see Section 6.2. They are also often fitted with integral temperate control valves which act via simple bimetallic springs which effectively switch-off most of the energy transfer from the absorber. However, heat-pipe collectors can only operate satisfactorily if they are inclined up greater than around 20 degrees from horizontal.

Where a tube collector does not have a heat-pipe, the primary fluid will enter inside the absorber which is inside the glass tube, see Figure 4.3. This places greater requirements on the durability of this fluid as the temperatures here can be exceptionally high. Without a heat-pipe, the tube collector can usually function when laid horizontal although some variations still require an inclination.

Reflectors are sometimes used internally or externally to increase the aperture that encourages further solar radiation to enter the tubes, see also Section 4.1.4.

4.1.3   Collector certification

Solar collectors should be fully tested and independently certified to BS EN 12975 in respect of durability, reliability and performance. This standard sets out procedures to test durability and reliability under extreme conditions, and provides a measure of energy performance. Where the collector falls within the scope of the Pressure Equipment Regulations and is tested by a notified body, then it can also show the 'CE' mark where compliance to the Pressure Equipment or other Directive is declared within the single European market. Optionally, these tests can be undertaken by accredited independent specialised test centres who are able to test and certify to this standard to show that the collector tested was randomly selected from a production line. This permits the use of the 'Solar Keymark' logo as shown in Figure 4.4.

Figure 4.4 Logos of the Solar Keymark and the 'CE' mark

4.1.4   Collector areas

The overall physical area of a collector is the gross area, this being the overall size. The area of the absorber within the collector frame is the net area. The aperture area is the unshaded opening that permits or reflects light in. Care must be taken in comparisons that the same data are being used. The net absorber area is a strong indication of the useful heat gathering surface potential. However in the case of some cylindrical tube absorbers; a reflector may also be present. In this case the aperture figure would have to be considered but, in the UK, reflectors are of limited benefit due to a rapid build up of mould and the strong effect of cloud cover diffusing the sunlight. Reflectors can also adversely affect the appearance of a collector that can otherwise be of a dark or neutral appearance.

4.1.5   Collector data badge

According to BE EN 12975, the collector would be expected to carry a data plate clearly displaying the following information:

● Manufacturer's name

● Serial no

● Year of production

● Country of production

● Type i.e. name of model

● Dimensions of collector

● Gross collector area

● Maximum stagnation temperature at 1000 W/m² and 30°C ambient

- Maximum operating pressure

- Fluid content

- Physical weight of each collector when empty

Where the collector is designed to be lifted without removing the packaging, the combined weight of the collector and packaging should be indicated on the outside of the packaging.

4.2 Collector performance

4.2.1 Collector efficiencies

The performance of a collector is strongly affected by its absorber (net) size and efficiency. For most solar DHW applications, it is possible to compensate for a low efficiency collector by increasing its size. However, where temperatures that are regularly in excess of 60°C are required in the secondary circuit, such as when combined with solar space heating applications in spring and autumn, then a high efficiency collector is best able to deliver higher temperatures. For a low temperature application, below 30°C, such as swimming pool heating, then a low efficiency collector can suffice.

4.2.2 Standardised test data

Performance is measured at a specialised test centre to BS EN 12975, by means of a plot of efficiency versus temperature difference, see Figure 4.5. The temperature difference, delta T, is the difference between the ambient air temperature and the average temperature of the collector. It is important to note that all types of collector start with similar efficiency when the collector is cold. However, as the collector begins to operate, it inevitably becomes hotter and hence its 'optical' efficiency drops. A high efficiency collector remains reasonably efficient even at hot collector temperatures. Evacuated tube collectors remain particularly efficient under a large delta T.

As well as the raw efficiency of the collector, the BS EN 12975 test also gives an indication of the following variables:

- Dynamic fluid pressure drop

- Thermal inertia - response rate to variable conditions

- Power output - rate of energy from collector

- Insulation of non-glazed areas via a U-value

These results can be used directly in predictive software and other calculations that assess monthly or annual performance.

The use of advanced special coatings on the absorber surface of the collector, assists the efficiency by reducing 're-emittance'. This occurs since the sun's energy falls to the earth at mostly short wavelengths typically less than 2.5 micrometers and this is often

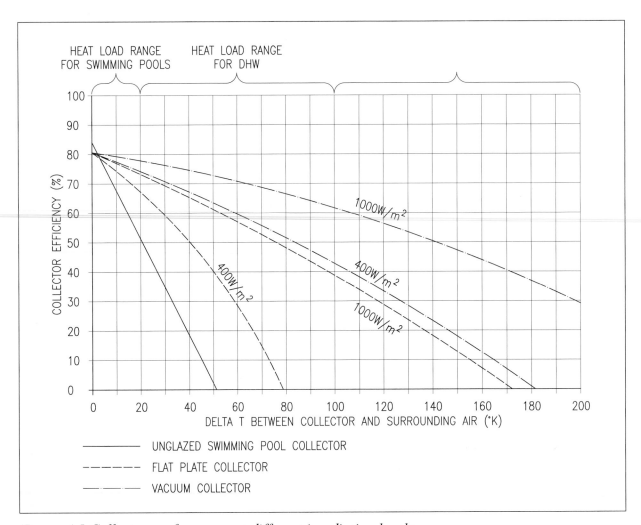

Figure 4.5 Collector performance at different irradiation levels

re-radiated or reflected back out at longer wavelengths, typically greater than 2.5 micrometers. This effect is more pronounced as the absorber becomes hotter. If a collector is to be highly efficient, it must inevitably make use of such 'selective' coatings since this will reduce this loss of energy re-radiated back out of the glazing hence improving the overall transfer of solar radiation, but without affecting the absorption.

There is little difference between the absorbing properties of selective and non-selective coatings. However there is nearly a tenfold difference in the re-emitting properties above 2.5 micrometres. Figure 4.6 indicates that the energy of the solar spectrum arrives mostly below 2.5 micrometres but is re-admitted mostly above this threshold. Some selective surfaces are sensitive to moisture and other contaminants, hence are generally factory applied and then sealed inside the collector. The appearance of a selective coating compared to that of simple black paint is that of a semi-translucent matt, blue/black hue, with no visible thickness.

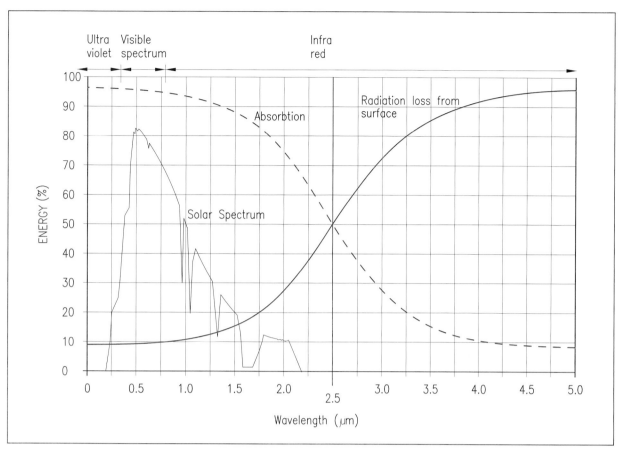

Figure 4.6 The wavelength spectrum of heat & properties of selective coatings

4.3   Solar Storage

4.3.1   Solar heat store methods

A successful solar DHW system requires the solar heat to be stored in a vessel to allow the heat to build-up slowly during the day. Most vessels used for solar storage use water although the use of other fluids or even solids is being researched. Because of the pattern of solar gain, it is very likely that an back-up heat source will also have to be integrated into the system. It is an early strategic choice as to whether to combine the outputs of both back-up and solar heat sources into one storage vessel. Using a single vessel, as shown in Figure 4.7, is the most common solution adopted in the UK and Ireland which is where a cylinder is fitted with two indirect coils, one heated by solar, the other heated by a boiler. There may also be an electric immersion heater in the storage vessel.

The other frequently adopted alternative is to use a solar storage vessel that is without any input from the back-up heat source. This vessel stands alone as a store that can then be used to pre-heat the water feeding the downstream heat store connected to the boiler, see Figure 4.8.

Back-up heat sources are fitted 'downstream' of the solar pre-heat storage to ensure that the back-up heat sources do not interfere with low temperature heat transfer from the solar primary circuit. It should be noted that a solar DHW collector works most efficiently at

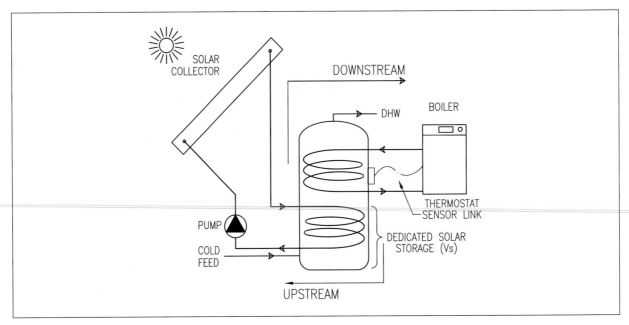

Figure 4.7 Combined solar store and DHW store

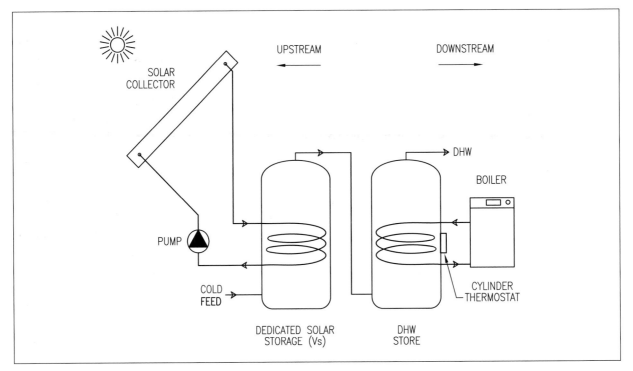

Figure 4.8 Separate solar store pre-heating DHW store

lower temperatures of less than 50°C, hence it is important to not let the higher temperatures from back-up heat source interfere with the solar primary. It also prevents back-up heat from accidentally circulating up to the collector where it would be lost.

This pre-heat method can also sometimes be used with an instantaneous heating appliance, such as a combi-boiler, providing the manufacturer approves the boiler for pre-heating, see Section 4.5.

4.3.2   Operation of solar storage systems

In the case of a combined storage vessel with twin coils, the back-up heat can be considered 'downstream' from the solar input, provided the solar coil is fitted near the base of the store below the top coil or electric immersion heater element. When DHW is drawn off from a combined store, water from the cold feed first enters at the base of the store and displaces solar pre-heated water which moves up into the top part of the store for any back-up heating that may be required. Natural buoyancy will ensure warm solar water will naturally rise up into the top part of the store.

In the case of a combined store, the two indirect coils must remain adequately separated vertically to ensure a sufficient and dedicated pre-heat volume is available for solar storage during all hours. With this proviso, the twin-coil store can remain as a 'hot-top' at all times to ensure user comfort and safety whilst the solar is automatically fed in below. A twin coil cylinder that has adjacent coils, instead of vertically separated coils, is not normally suitable for solar heating.

4.4   Solar store stratification

The stratification of water at various temperature levels in a solar store is vital for the high efficiency of the solar primary circuit. Stratification arises from the natural layering of water at different densities, where the hottest water rises to the top and the coolest descends to the bottom, see Figure 4.9. This layering forms as the solar circuit heats the store and it is advantageous that the return of the primary circuit remains cool for as long as possible throughout the day. With a cool return, the collector will have lower heat losses and will readily absorb more heat from the sun's radiation. In a well designed system, the return temperature of the solar circuit will only rise above 50°C once the whole store has heated from top to bottom. As water is drawn off through the secondary system, the cold feed will assist the stratification by bringing in more cool water, but only if a baffle plate is located to prevent the inrush from causing unwanted turbulence. Similarly unwanted turbulence from secondary circulation pumps, boiler coils or powerful immersion heaters can all serve to disrupt stratification.

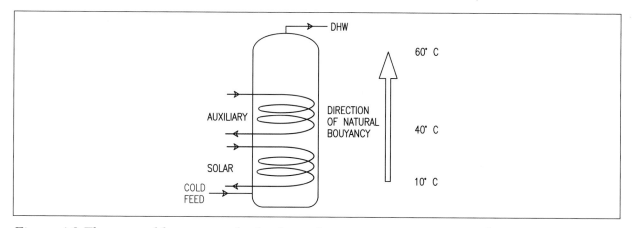

Figure 4.9 The natural buoyancy of solar heated warm water creates stratification

If the secondary water remains static over many hours, then heat conduction through the walls of the cylinder (heat-creep) can also disrupt stratification. This is especially an issue for thermal stores where the cold feed does not strongly assist stratification. Some special stores use internal plates or funnels to encourage stable stratification. Whilst stratification remains useful for solar stores, this may be different for DHW stores where it is sometimes purposefully designed in to increase storage capacity or reduce unheated areas.

4.5   Pre heating of water used in instantaneous DHW appliances

The pre-heating of water used in 'instantaneous' DHW appliances must be considered with great care, as many of these types of appliance are not designed to receive heated water. In all cases, the manufacturers of the appliances must be contacted for advice before this type of system is installed. Typically, the designers of such appliances originally expected the cold feed to be no more than 25°C. Such appliances include combi-boilers, single point, electrical point-of-use and multi-point water heaters. The supply of solar pre-heated water to these appliances when the manufacturer does not approve the practice can lead to the appliance working inefficiently, overheating and even result in component failure. A thermostatic blending valve may well be required for protection, sometimes on both inlet and outlet of the appliance. Some appliances may display a mark to indicate suitability for pre-heating, when the internal components have been tested to a higher temperature, which is indicated as part of the mark. This type of installation is not recommended and is covered below for information purposes only. Layouts which utilise specialised 'solar-ready' instantaneous water heaters are illustrated in Figures 4.10 and 4.11. Note these indicate the use of a thermostatic link to avoid unnecessary operation of the downstream appliance once the solar storage has reached at least 60°C and in some case 70°C. See also Section 5.7.

During the draw-off of small volumes of hot water from these systems, correct thermostatic control is essential to ensure that the appliance does not switch on or fire unnecessarily when the solar store is already sufficiently hot. A thermostat with a remote sensor attached to the store is required to control the instantaneous appliance and

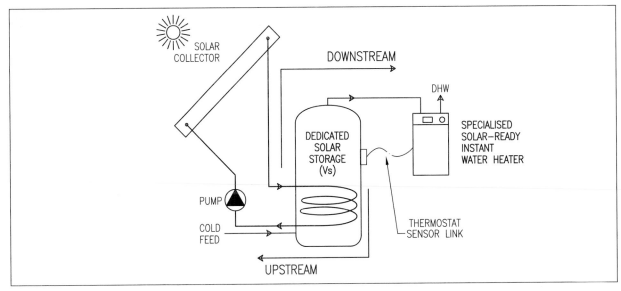

Figure 4.10 Schematic pipework and control layout for a solar store providing pre-heating for an instant DHW heater

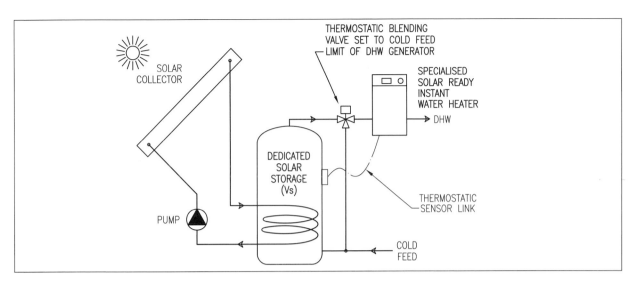

Figure 4.11 Schematic pipework and control layout for solar pre heating an instantaneous DHW heater with cold feed limit

respond to the solar heat prior to draw-off. This will prevent the instantaneous appliance firing if the solar store is hot enough. The appliance should always remain able to provide sufficient temperature to ensure comfort and sterilisation in varying conditions. In any case, this type of installation should only be undertaken with prior written confirmation that the boiler is suitable.

Diversion valves that enable the solar heated water to by-pass the instantaneous water heater when the solar water is hot enough can, under fault conditions, allow untreated water into the DHW distribution and can put the user at increased risk from scalding. Such systems must be accompanied by additional thermostatic protection, from the solar primary controls or from the thermostatic blending valves.

It should be noted that both diversion and thermostatic valves placed in the secondary system require regular maintenance, especially in high limescale risk areas. They can also inadvertently block important safety features such as expansion backflow from water heaters and so should only be included with the full approval of the manufacturer of the instantaneous appliance. See also Section 5.7 for matters concerning legionella with such valves. However, where correctly fitted with a thermostatic link in pre-heated systems, diverter valves can increase overall appliance energy performance particularly during high solar gains by avoiding the loss of solar heat as it passes through the cold metalwork of the boiler.

Where prescribed by a manufacturer, a thermostatic blending valve can protect the cold feed of an instantaneous water heater, see Figure 4.11. It should be noted that where such valves are only used to protect in fault situations, they can remain inoperative for the majority of their life. This can present an increased risk in bacterial growth as the water in the cold inlet would remain static for long periods at tepid temperatures. Where faced with an existing combi boiler, it may be possible to adapt the system as shown in Figure 7.1. Here a twin-coil, unvented hot water store is used to replace the DHW originally supplied by the combi. The top coil of the store is now heated as part of a new heating zone and the combi is in effect operating like a regular boiler. The full written support of the combi manufacturer must be sought before making such changes.

5   Working principles

5.1   Solar thermal power availability against loading

The primary circuit of a solar DHW system is designed with a storage vessel because most typical DHW loads far exceed the size and power of a typical solar collector, even during full sunshine, see Table 5.1. Hence, the storage becomes vital to allow solar heated water to be accumulated in sufficient quantities to provide a satisfactory level of DHW. Moreover, the relationship of the supply of solar energy and the demand for DHW by the consumer is rarely coincidental. However, if the heat is built up gradually into a store during the day, not only is the temperature raised higher but also the volume of heated stored water becomes greater. The proportion of the total DHW load which can be met by the solar system is known as the solar fraction. By the end of a 'good' summer day, a well-designed system can fulfil 100% of the day's DHW requirements in the UK and Ireland. Thereafter, for the rest of the year or during inclement weather, there will be a shortfall of daily energy available from the solar system, which must be met from other sources. See also Section 7.5.6.

Whilst it is possible to 'oversize' a collector to gain greater coverage in the spring and autumn, this can present over-heating problems in summer and reduced cost-effectiveness. During winter, the performance of a Solar DHW system is considerably lower than in the summer, as on average, only a fifth of the energy is available.

The use of solar energy to pre-heat DHW is the predominant active use of solar heat in the UK and Ireland, but there are applications for space heating as well. However, in this case, careful thought must be given to the availability of the solar energy in

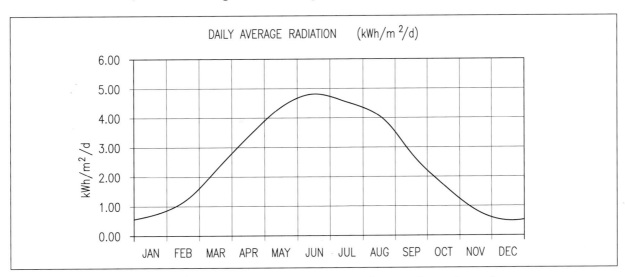

Figure 5.1 Chart to illustrate the distribution of solar radiation throughout the year

Parameter	Range	Notes
Peak irradiation falling horizontally on ground	1.0 - 1.2 kW/m²	Highest peaks occur briefly during sunbursts.
Peak power at solar collector	0.7 kW/ m²	Highest peaks occur briefly during sunbursts in the plane of useful collecting surface
Peak optical efficiency of modern solar collectors	Over 80%	Highest peaks occur briefly during sunbursts emerging after a cold period behind dark clouds. A measure of incident radiation to thermal conversion
Peak overall solar DHW system efficiency	50%	A measure of incident radiation to useful energy at the taps
Peak daily irradiation energy	5 - 7 kWh/m²	Summer peaks measured horizontally
Annual irradiation energy UK	800 - 1100 kWh/m²	Incident radiation measured horizontally
Typical useful energy from solar DHW system	350 - 450 kWh/m²	Overall useful energy at taps at 55°C, annual average per net collector area
Typical DHW annual solar fraction @ stored target of 60°C	40 - 60%	Assuming non-solar back-up
Peak DHW and space heating solar fraction	Less than 15 %	Assuming non-solar back-up

Table 5.1 Typical performance values of solar DHW

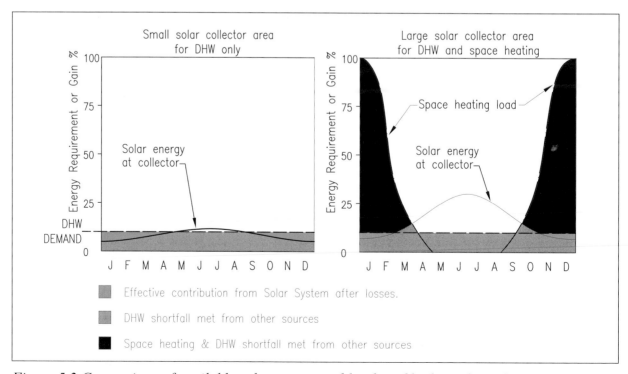

Figure 5.2 Comparison of available solar energy and load profile throughout the year

relationship to the demand, (or load). Whereas the demand for DHW at 55°C is consistent in most buildings through the year, the demand for space heating swings heavily from large peaks in winter to negligible in summer. In particular during cold winter nights, the quantity of solar energy is at its lowest; hence the space heating load at these times must be met by conventional fuels. See Figures 5.1 and 5.2.

The temperature of the consumed DHW used at taps, baths, showers etc., is assumed to be 45°C for the purposes of calculations. However, this is the blended temperature with cold water at the point of use. This compares to DHW in the distribution pipes which should be at no less than 55°C and the storage temperature should be no less than 60°C, see Section 5.7. Statements of solar performance must make clear what assumptions of temperature and volume of DHW were made. See also Section 2.2.

System efficiencies

As with conventional heating systems, there are energy losses involved in all stages of heat transfer in a solar DHW system, as shown in Figure 5.3. A well designed system attempts to minimise these losses. For example, the benefits of a more expensive, high efficiency collector would be lost unless the pipes and store were equally upgraded. Also, the relationship between the sizes of components should be considered, particularly for the sizes of the solar collector and the storage vessel.

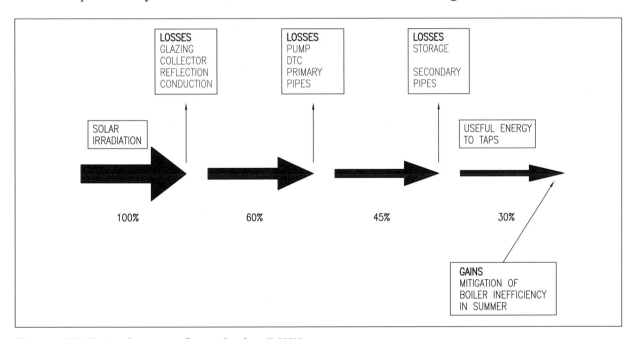

Figure 5.3 Typical energy flow of solar DHW system

5.2   Direct and diffuse irradiation

The UK climate has a high percentage of cloudy days when the sunlight is dispersed as it passes though or around the clouds. Such light is termed diffuse whereas sunlight without such dispersion is called direct. Solar collectors are able to receive both types of light. During the winter, the sun is more frequently lower in the sky and so must pass more obliquely though the atmosphere. The effects of particulates, either man-made or natural, also contribute to the diffuse effect.

As well as the above consideration, the sun's energy passes into the atmosphere in both visible narrow band, and non-visible wide band form. The entire 'spectrum' falls onto a collector and so it can be said that collectors can work with daylight as well as sunlight. That said, direct sunlight is far stronger at around 1.0 kW/m² daily compared to a cloudy day that may only provide 0.2 kW/m² – see Figures 5.1 and 5.4. It is the sum of both direct and diffuse solar energy that permits solar systems to achieve a reasonable annual performance.

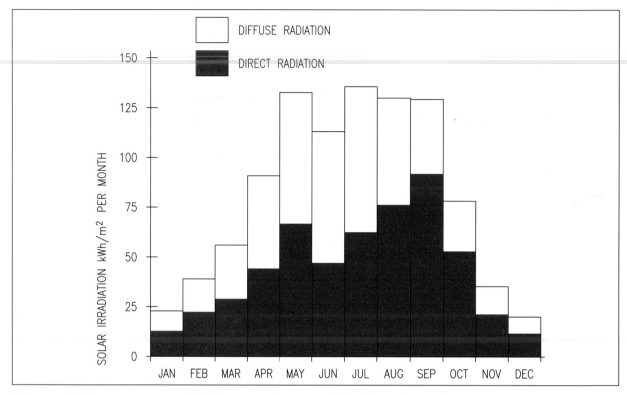

Figure 5.4 The proportion of diffuse and direct sunlight throughout the year

5.3   Positioning of collectors

The compass direction (orientation) and the angle of the collector from the horizontal (degree of tilt) affects the annual quantity of energy collected. The optimum irradiation available from the sun lies between at an orientation between south east and south west at a tilt of 30 to 40 degrees from horizontal, as shown in Figure 5.5, which indicates the variation in radiation according to the tilt and orientation. At this angle of tilt, an orientation between East and West will still yield 80% of the optimum annual energy. A horizontally positioned collector will also normally yield 80% of the optimum annual energy. Using large collectors can compensate for most of the losses resulting from positioning below the optimum; however, positions facing at angles to the North are to be avoided where possible. Where a collector is to be mounted on a pitched roof, the choice of angle is in effect already fixed, however, for flat roofs or ground-mounted collectors the full choice is possible. Steep angles promote winter gains for space heating and reduce dust accumulation. Tube collectors can often be internally rotated to improve the angle of the absorber.

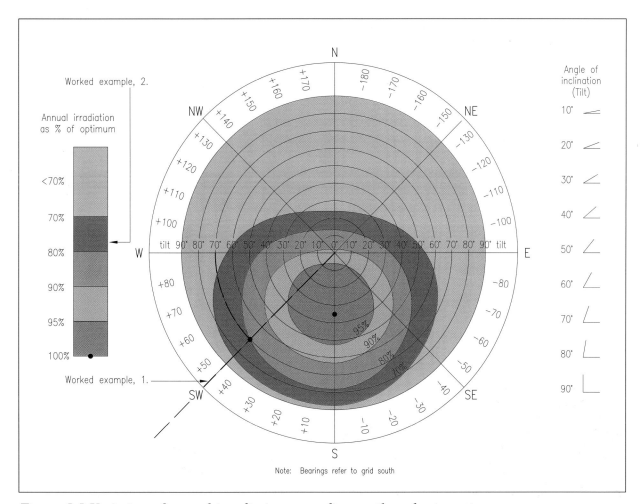

Figure 5.5 Variation of annual irradiation according to tilt and orientation

Whilst the annual useful energy output of a collector is strongly related to the annual irradiation relationship shown in Figures 5.2 and 5.5, it should be noted that this becomes less relevant in high performance systems with a large solar fraction, see also Section 7.5.6. Here, where the system is already assumed to provide 100% summer DHW, any further increase in summer gains has no useful effect, but the benefit is shown by an increase in gains during spring and autumn. For these reasons the values in Figure 5.5 should be used with caution in respect of high solar fraction systems. This point can be further appreciated by studying Figure 5.2 where it can be seen that a larger collector area on the right-hand chart makes the extra gains in spring/autumn because the summer period is already largely satisfied even by a modest collector area.

A great deal of solar gain can be lost due to shading, even where the collector is otherwise in an optimum location. Shading can occur briefly, perhaps from a telephone mast or be persistent throughout winter, such as from a nearby hill. Since solar radiation falls as much indirectly as directly, the effect of shading is not a complete loss of solar gain but it should never the less be avoided wherever possible. Table 5.2 permits a quantification of the shading effect and Figure 5.6 indicates the angles of the sun tracks that change with the seasons.

Worked example:

A roof pitch is measured to have a tilt of 70° inclination (i.e. up from horizontal) and orientation of 45° West of South i.e. South-West.

1. On Figure 5.5, use a ruler to line up South-West (+45°) on the outer white ring of the circle and strike a line from this value to the centre of the circle.

2. Taking away the ruler, identify the concentric circle that represents the tilt of 70° and follow the concentric circle around until it intersects the above line. (shown as a dotted line in the example) .

3. Identify the colour in the area of the intersection (i.e. example is purple/mauve). Identify this colour on the annual irradiation bar scale. This can be seen to be approximately 80%. Hence a loss of 20% can be expected on this roof compared to the optimum of due South at roof pitch 40° (centre of red circle).

Over shading	% of sky blocked by obstacles	Over shading factor	Examples
Heavy	> 80%	0.5	Large hill or tower block causing obstruction of spring/autumn sun
Significant	> 60% - 80%	0.65	Loss of winter sun from hill, tower block or multiple coniferous trees
Modest	20% - 60%	0.8	Chimney, dormer, adjacent roof and multiple deciduous trees
None or very little	< 20%	1.0	Telegraph pole or single deciduous tree

Table 5.2 Shading factors

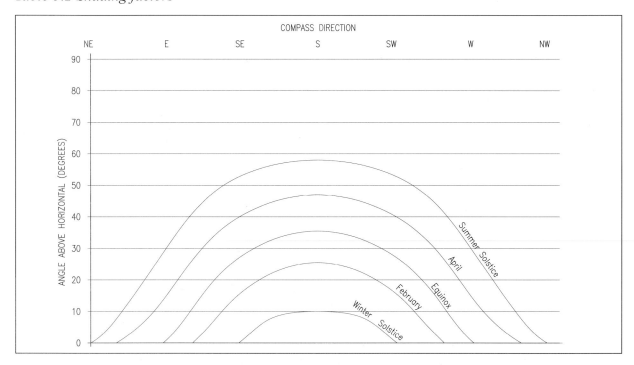

Figure 5.6 Seasonal sun paths at 56°N

5.4   Protecting from freeze damage

Since part of a solar heating system must be located externally, there is inevitably a risk of freeze damage to components. When plain water freezes, it becomes solid and expands causing the following problems:

● Circulation to cease

● Fracture of rigid materials

● Blockage of routes for venting or discharge

There are various methods found to address these problems:

5.4.1   Antifreeze

This is the most common method. It involves the use of special high temperature, low-toxicity chemicals based on aqueous polypropylene glycol. Antifreeze used in motor vehicles is based on ethylene glycol, which is highly toxic and must not be used near domestic water. Antifreeze, if added alone, increases the risk of corrosion, hence must be used with corrosion inhibitors and then only in indirect circuits. Some old systems used special oil although this is now difficult to obtain. Antifreeze concentrations require regular testing of acidity and glycol levels. Where a fully filled, sealed system is required to operate without release of liquid or vapour under any operating conditions, the antifreeze and inhibitor solutions are required to be able to readily reverse between the liquid and the evaporation phases without leaving insoluble deposits. See also Section 5.5. Although polypropylene glycol is low toxicity and readily biodegradable, it should not be assumed that old antifreeze can simply be disposed into public sewers without checking with the local water utility. It should be noted that antifreeze or chemical corrosion inhibitors must not be used in direct primary systems as they will become quickly diluted and possibly cause health problems if ingested.

5.4.2   Auto pump control

This is triggered by a collector temperature sensor with an adjustable minimum setting which runs the pump when the temperature drops below the set temperature. This method should only be considered if freezing is expected for only a few days a year, due to electric pump energy losses each time it switches on. However, it leaves the system very vulnerable during power cuts or pump failure.

5.4.3   Drain back

By only partially filling the primary circuit and retaining an air pocket in it, the primary fluid can be drained back from the external components into the warmer interior of the building by switching off the pump. The pump requires either a temperature control or one based on solar radiation levels set at minimum levels. For extra security, antifreeze can also be used in the circuit. This type of system requires careful design and installation work to ensure that the pipes always fall back to the special drainback vessel. This method is very common in some Northern European countries.

5.4.4   Auto drain down

A mechanical valve controlled by a bi-metallic lever is located at a low level in the circuit. This opens to dump the fluid contents of the system when the temperature is near freezing point. Skilled personnel are required to refill and recommission after operation hence this system is rarely used. It is mainly suitable for use in warmer climates with very occasional freezing. This system should not be used unless such skilled assistance is readily available.

5.4.5   Freeze tolerant materials

System installation materials are chosen that are able to accommodate the expansion caused by freezing and remain flexible in cold temperatures e.g. plastic or rubber. Accompanying joints and components that could be rigid when cold need to be avoided or they will require other protection methods. In particular, safety vent pipes leading from the collector or similar devices must continue to work if any part of the system fluid freezes. Such flexible materials should be carefully considered in relation to Building Regulation 7 in England and Wales, which concerns materials and workmanship. Accordingly, non-metallic, flexible components in solar circuits that can foreseeably contain steam and survive rodent attack should be carefully verified for fitness of purpose. Extra protection from vermin attack is likely to be required.

5.4.6   Insulation

Used primarily to conserve heat and meet the requirements of the Water and Building Regulations. Insulation never eliminates the chance of freezing over a long period of very low temperatures.

5.5   High temperature conditions

Although the peak power of the sun, at 1 kW/m², may initially appear to be modest compared to power outputs from fossil fuel heating appliances, it should not be forgotten that solar is a renewable energy source, which is largely uncontrolled, and yet can quickly accumulate enough heat in a high performance collector to convert the circulating liquid to steam under significant pressure. Since the worst-case scenarios inevitably generate steam, primary solar systems should be designed for steam handling from the outset.

Sometimes a high temperature situation arises during a circulation failure, i.e. a faulty pump, power cut, or even as part of normal operation under thermostatic primary or storage safety controls. Whatever the reason, both the primary and secondary system may overheat. The state in which there is no net heat extraction from the collector is described as 'stagnation'. If the collector is not designed for the 'stagnation' temperature, it can be considered to be over-heated and potentially unsafe.

Historically, older systems lost their excess heat through poorly insulated cylinders and pipework or even by boiling the DHW store in order to dissipate this excess heat. As collectors became more efficient and stores better insulated, such methods became less effective and excess heat solutions had to be dealt with by design. Modern equipment can create steam in excessive quanitities and at times become potentially unsafe. In some operational contexts, after such use, the system requires re-commissioning to re-fill the primary system and return normal circulation.

Modern solar primary systems can be designed and installed to automatically and safely resume normal operation after an excess temperature event as specified in paragraph 4.1.4 of BS EN 12976 by meeting the following criteria:

● No release of any high temperature fluid (vapour or liquid) under any operating conditions

● Auto-resumption of normal operation after stagnation, without end-user intervention

A liquid based primary circulation system meeting these criteria is termed 'hydraulically secure' and this can be achieved with sealed, indirect primary systems that contain a vessel capable of holding the primary fluid contents of the collector at all the permitted pressures in the system. This vessel can be of the membrane expansion type or of the drainback air-pocket type.

Such systems require careful choices of equipment and installation skills but have the advantage that the sun can be reliably 'turned off', which was not possible in earlier system designs. In 'hydraulically secure' systems, all materials in contact with primary system fluids, as well as components such as pipe clips and pipe insulation must be rated to withstand the full collector stagnation temperature when pressurised. See also Table 7.17. They must also be protected against rodent attack and UV degradation, particularly those parts located externally. Many common plumbing materials will quickly fail under these severe conditions so specialised components specifically designed for use in solar thermal systems are called for. See also 7.12.

Where a system is fully filled and designed to be 'hydraulically secure', the system pressure settings are varied to permit a chosen 'boil' point in the collector. This is the temperature point of the antifreeze at which the fluid will vaporise. It is vital that this is not chosen so high as to cause premature chemical breakdown of the antifreeze. Typically, between 120°C and 130°C is chosen, although the collector absorber without any fluid will attain a much higher temperature. The pump control settings are also adjusted to prevent intentional circulation beyond the boil point, see Appendix C. Where the collector area is designed to be larger than that supplying half the annual domestic hot water demands, such as with space heating assistance, the frequency of stagnation in summer will increase as the average demand for heat drops. This causes a greater strain on the antifreeze, which should be tested regularly for concentration and acidity. The removal of flux and oxygen from the system is paramount to the long-term durability of glycol antifreeze, especially when heated to high temperatures in the collector.

New fluids are being developed which will enable higher boil points to be designed for in the future. Caution should be taken with some alcohol-based additives, as there can be an increased flammability risk near sources of ignition.

Drainback systems require fewer requirements from the properties of their primary fluids as they operate at lower pressure and temperature. Where plain water is used the inherent oxygen content will react with any steel surfaces in the system, thereafter the water should remain stable over many years. However, if there is any re-filling due to leaks, then the same consideration of the use of antifreeze and corrosion inhibiters will be required as with fully-filled systems. This will also be the case where the drainback vessel is located in an area where there is a freezing risk. See also Section 3.5 and 5.4.

5.6   Limescale

Hot water stores connected indirectly to solar systems and to direct solar water collectors are all vulnerable to the formation of lime-scale. Left unchecked, and without proper control, the life and performance of heating systems will be steadily, perhaps dramatically, reduced where fresh hard water is continually passed through pipes, heat exchangers and collectors. This undermines the performance and durability of equipment complying with solar standards BS EN 12975 and BS EN 12976. Installations in hard water areas can provide disappointing energy gains and give rise to requests for premature replacement. Limescale deposition particularly affects solar systems due to the high temperatures frequently obtained both in the primary and secondary stores. Even where water softeners or conditioners are used, the excessive temperatures can exceed their normal tolerances.

Limescale is site specific and risk has to be assessed accordingly. The measures required may include:

- Obtaining a water quality report from water utility
- Viewing inside a kettle, shower rose or hot taps in premises
- Chemical analysis of water on the premises
- Checking for the installation of a water softener

Keeping components in contact with secondary water to below 60°C can reduce limescale deposition although this often conflicts with bacterial protection. Adequate sizing and using indirect solar primary systems can achieve this, however, this can conflict with legionella control methods. Providing a means to physically remove scale deposition, where it is expected to form, is a sensible measure to design in. This could include cleaning hatches located at the heat exchanger or using demountable plate exchangers, although these are normally only seen in steel vessels.

5.7   Sterilisation of bacteria

The subject of legionella bacteria is covered extensively in CIBSE TM13: Minimising the Risk of Legionnaire's Disease, and Health and Safety Executive ACOP L8. At certain times, according to the weather and water throughput, the secondary consumable water is likely to be at temperatures of between 20°C and 46°C when storing solar heat. This temperature permits conditions for the multiplication of bacteria and great care must be given as to how such pre-heated water is treated. Pre-heated water straight from solar stores should not be considered suitable for distribution as domestic hot

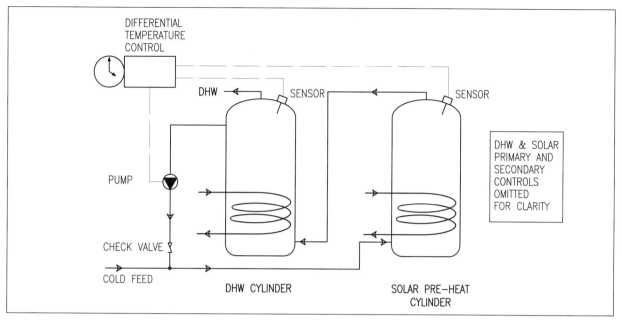

Figure 5.7 Schematic layout of pipework and controls for daily disinfection of a separate solar pre heat store

water until its temperature has been raised to a sufficient level to kill any bacteria. At 60°C, bacteria can survive for only minutes whereas at 70°C the bacteria in the water are killed instantaneously. Solar DHW storage systems where water has been left in storage for more than a day at temperatures of less than 50°C are more likely to be at risk.

The temperatures noted above can be used to treat pre-heated secondary water, although this may then present a scalding risk. See also Section 6.3.1. High temperatures can also encourage limescale formation and accelerated metallic corrosion with some water types. The design and arrangement of a solar pre-heat system therefore requires a skilful balance in order to select a suitable target temperature that will control bacteria, even during high draw-off rates.

Water sterilization for showers is particularly important because of the aerosol effect of these appliances. A particular scenario, which requires very careful consideration, is the use of a shower with a high water flow rate, which could cause pre-heated water to pass rapidly through a back-up heater and not reach the target sterilisation temperature. The use of flow limiters to maintain a target temperature may be required, particularly in the case of instantaneous DHW generators such as combi-boilers or single point electric heaters.

Where a stored DHW arrangement is used, the use of a combined store, as indicated in Section 4.3.1, easily permits a constant 60°C 'hot-top' and hence provides the minimum bacterial risk since natural buoyancy causes pre-heated water to automatically rise up the store into the sterilised zone, irrespective of DHW draw-off regime. Using a thermostat, interlocked to a back-up heat source, will ensure that all water intended for draw off reaches the target temperature. The volume of the stored DHW, the power of the back-up heat store and response of the thermostat should be matched to ensure that the maximum foreseeable draw-off rate does not permit untreated water to pass through.

In the case of separate solar pre-heat stores, as shown in Figure 4.8, the warm water would normally be sterilised only during or just after draw-off providing the downstream DHW store is maintained at its target temperature under all foreseeable draw-off rates. Any attempt to use a back-up heat source or re-circulation in the solar store would risk loss of dedicated solar storage and reduction of the collector efficiency so this should be carefully considered as indicated below and also Figure 5.7 and Section 7.

Automatic diverter valves are sometimes used with a separate pre-heat cylinder and are referred to as 'Sun-to-tap' systems. This arrangement must be approached with caution particularly with motorised valves, for the following reasons:

- It places too great a reliance on the accuracy of thermostats

- The motorised valve or thermostat may fail with the valve in the open position

- Possible incompatibility of motorised valve materials with secondary water

- The DHW cylinder may continue to heat to 60°C, irrespective of solar storage

The use of manual diverter valves such as user operated three-way valves cannot be recommended due to the risk of users misunderstanding their function or forgetting to return to pre-heat mode once the temperature drops.

Where a higher bacterial risk is identified, such as with large solar stores over 400 litres capacity, one solution for legionella control is the careful use of a timed secondary pump to move heat between the two stores (Figure 5.7) or within a combined store. This technique has two benefits in that the pre-heat store, or lower part of the store, can be regularly sterilised during the period when there is the smallest effect on solar gains typically between 4 and 6 pm immediately prior to the peak evening draw-off. In the case of a separate solar store, this technique also has the benefit of increasing solar storage during summer and reducing over-heating. This operation must be controlled by a Differential Temperature Control (DTC), see Section 6.1.3, with a built-in time clock to ensure that heat movement occurs both thermostatically according to the pre-heat store temperature and timed according the solar gains. Incorrect operation of the secondary pump will de-stratify the solar storage and raise its temperature to a point where the solar collector loses efficiency, see also Figure 7.9 and Section 7.7.

The pump should therefore be controlled to operate when either:

- The pre-heat cylinder has reached at least 60°C and is at a higher temperature than the DHW cylinder

- The pre-heat cylinder has not already reached 60°C by solar alone before late afternoon

The use of some low power or low temperature back-up heat sources such as solid fuel stoves or heat pumps may require an additional electric immersion heater to ensure sterilisation under peak draw off rates.

The use of secondary pumped circuits for the purposes of minimising cold water 'dead-legs' or bacterial growth, can unintentionally disturb the solar pre-heat volume unless the secondary return connection into the storage is carefully located. The preferred locations where integrated with solar storage are indicated in Figures 5.8 and 5.9. In the case of two separate stores, the secondary circulation can also facilitate movement of

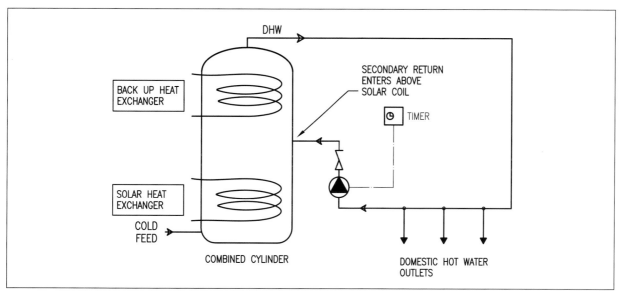

Figure 5.8 Schematic layout of pipework and time control for a pumped secondary circuit connected to a twin-coil solar store

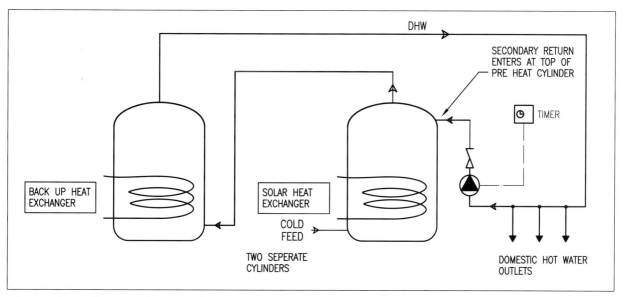

Figure 5.9 Schematic layout of pipework and time control for a pumped secondary circuit connected to a separate solar pre-heat store

solar heat into the back-up heater store which would otherwise only transfer during draw-off. In all cases, the secondary pump should be set to its lowest setting to avoid de-stratification of the pre-heat volume whilst still maintaining adequate circulation. Excessive use of secondary circulation pumps with poorly insulated pipework can significantly increase energy losses of solar and back-up heat sources. Their use should be carefully considered and in any case, controlled with use of timers and adequate insulation where ever possible.

5.8 Orientation of flow and return pipework

The orientation of the flow and return connections in a solar primary circuit is often a source of confusion, possibly due to the unusual location of some components. To maintain efficiency and eliminate air locks, the primary circuit should be connected correctly.

The principle that has to be borne in mind is that the flow will be the hottest pipe from the collector and the return will be the cooler. At the collector, therefore, the flow will be the highest pipe since this is where any heat will naturally accumulate from natural buoyancy as the sun's energy is collected. In a fully filled system, it makes sense to place the pump direction in harmony with this natural direction of heat flow and to assist the removal of air. Furthermore, it is normal to locate a collector temperature sensor at the hottest point in the absorber for control purposes. This sensor must not be located near the return inlet otherwise there would be a possibility of short cycling. See also Section 6.1.3. As the pump circulates, cool return fluid is pushed up through the collector removing hot fluid from the top and around the circuit down towards the cylinder heat exchanger, see Figure 5.10.

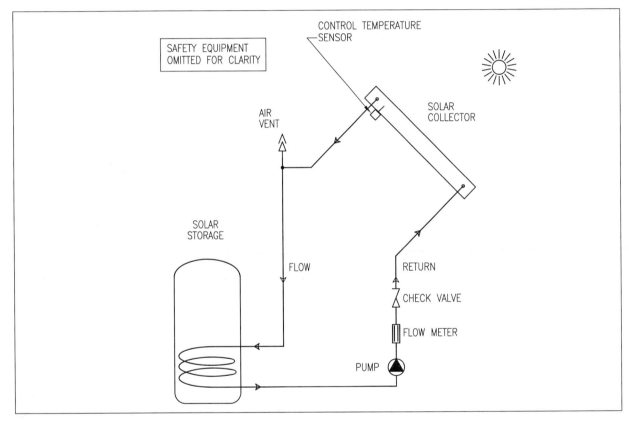

Figure 5.10 Simple schematic layout of a solar primary circuit

Historically, the flow connection from boilers has been connected to the top tapping of an internal coil since many older systems were based on thermo-siphoning. Similarly with pumped solar primary circuits it remains essential to pump down the coil to ensure the return to the collector will be from the coolest point near the cold feed, this being the lowest tapping in the solar store. The natural stratification of the store will ensure this point is kept cool as heat will normally rise upwards displacing cooler water. This method does conflict with the natural exit route for entrapped air in the coil, hence it is good practice to route the flow pipe, connected to the top of the coil, to rise constantly upwards to the air removal points and allow the pump to rest whilst purging. Extra air vents and even air separators are often required in fully filled systems to ensure all air is removed, and special commissioning techniques may be used, see also Section 9.2.

In certain solar primary systems, where air is constantly entrained with the fluid, such as those using drainback for frost protection, reversing the cylinder flow and return connections may help resolve some circulation problems, although at the expense of significant efficiency loss.

5.9   Solar input and losses

A well-designed household solar DHW system in the UK can expect to gain between 800-1750 kWh of useful energy per year. This figure will not be achieved in a poor installation, in part because of excessive losses in the pipework and storage. See Table 5.1.

Pipes transferring solar primary fluids occasionally carry temperatures in excess of 150°C. This is much higher than conventional DHW or boiler primary pipes and, if un-insulated, the pipes can lose over 10 per cent of the total annual useful solar energy, according to BS 5422. Furthermore, any solar thermal water heating system is defined by Building Regulations as a controlled service. It must therefore meet all the requirements of the Regulations, in particular in relation to Part L1a(ii) of the Regulations, which requires that storage vessels and pipework for hot water are adequately insulated.

A poorly insulated store can be expected to lose over 2 kWh per day, inclusive of boiler-heated water. This can amount to as much as the solar system can contribute. A good quality store would only lose half of this quantity. It is important to ensure that insulation around joints, bosses and fittings is not overlooked. The potential losses are summarised in Figure 5.11 and Table 5.3.

The electrical energy used in pumping water around the system, along with pump control devices, can amount to over 8 per cent of the total solar thermal energy that can be collected by the system. Part of this energy is recovered, either during the space heating season through the pump case, if the equipment is installed in the space-heated area, or into the pumped fluid that can regain about 40% of the lost energy. The electrical input power of the primary pump in the solar system should be designed to use no more than two per cent of the peak thermal power of the collector, the peak thermal power of a solar system is calculated at 0.7 kW per square metre of net absorber area.

To ensure that the 'downstream' heat source responds correctly to the solar heat gain, the contribution of any back-up heaters requires control with a temperature-sensing link to the solar storage. The control interlock will then ensure that the downstream appliance does not supply heat when the solar heated water has already reached its target temperature (at least 60°C).

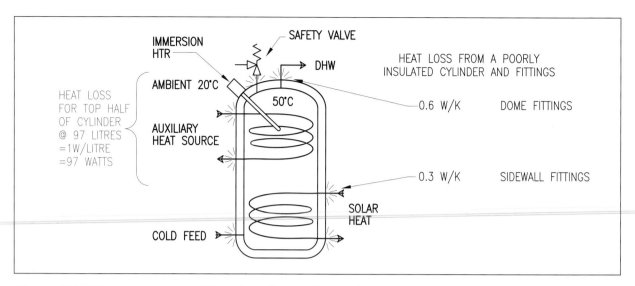

Figure 5.11 The importance of heat loss from cylinder fittings

Item	Number	Rate of heat loss (W/K)	ΔT (K)	Heat loss subtotals (W)
Top half cylinder to BS 1566	1	n/a	n/a	97
Dome fittings	3	0.6	30	57
Sidewall fittings	5	0.3	20	30
			TOTAL =	184

Table 5.3 Rate of heat loss from a poorly insulated cylinder

Worked example:

From Figure 5.9 and Table 5.3, the following calculation provides an estimate of the annual heat losses of a twin-coil cylinder.

Multiplying heat-loss for one year: 184 x 24 x 365 = 1611kWh

6   Controls

6.1   Circulation and temperature control

6.1.1   Safety and efficiency

A well-designed solar DHW system will possess controls for health and safety risks as well as those for operating efficiently. In addition, Part L1 of the Building Regulations requires that fixed building services are provided with adequate controls. Temperature and circulation measuring devices are particularly useful in a solar system and are sometimes built-in to the pump control system permitting both safe commissioning of the system and providing user information. Sometimes these controls are also capable of monitoring long-term performance and can anticipate operational problems.

The essential requirements of a control strategy are:

- Primary circulation
- Primary overpressure
- Primary expansion
- Secondary temperature

Primary temperature is not indicated as a control item because a solar system should be manufactured to survive all expected temperatures, from freezing through to stagnation, without reliance on control devices. Secondary expansion of DHW is a subject adequately covered in other guidance (WRAS/DEFRA Water Regulations Guide).

In considering how to apply a control strategy, it is also instructive to consider the key functional areas of a solar thermal system, which can be thought of as follows:

- Solar collection
- Primary circulation
- Solar heat storage
- Back-up DHW system
- Primary circulation control

These functions can be designed to intergrate with the operation of a back-up DHW heating appliance without restricting comfort or unduly increasing risks, see Figure 6.1.

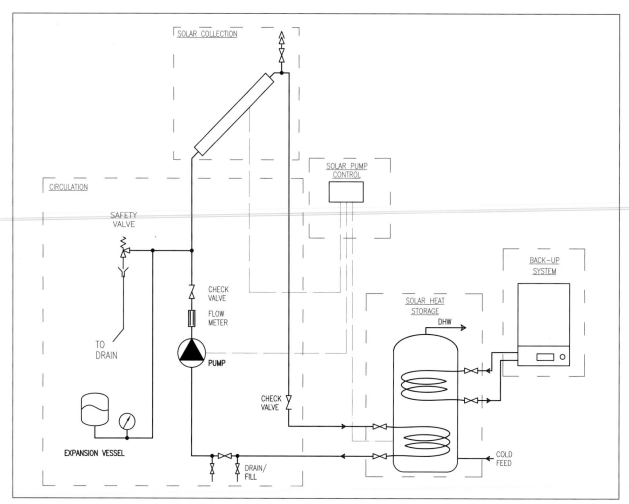

Figure 6.1 Schematic to show relationship between the different functional areas of a solar system

6.1.2   Primary circulation control

Circulation is principally about the control of the circulating pump and the effect this has on the system efficiency. If circulation is at the incorrect rate or indeed ceases completely, then the system should be designed so that the consequences do not affect the health and safety of the system or its users. It follows that by designing the hydraulic components to meet BS EN 12976, as described in later sections of this chapter, then a system should not require the user to interact to return the system to normal operation after a stagnation incident. This, in turn, implies that any loss of circulation, whether intentional or by fault, should not cause any fluid contents to leave the solar primary circuit, even under stagnation conditions.

Assuming this requirement is met and the system is designed to be 'hydraulically secure', the pump no longer has to simply operate when the collector is hot. Pump operation is also related to:

- Maximising collector efficiency
- Minimizing pipe losses
- Maximising heat exchanger efficiency
- Minimising storage losses

It should be also noted that any controls in contact with the primary circuit should be suitable for the range of temperatures, pressures and fluid types generally experienced in solar primary systems. In particular, temperatures well in excess of 150°C can be expected in or near to solar collectors, see also Section 7.12.

6.1.3   Differential temperature control

Since solar heating essentially involves the moving of heat by a pump, a sensible control method for the pump to improve efficiency will involve measurement and comparison of temperature as shown in Figure 6.2. Water circulation should normally only be activated when the temperature in the collector is above that of the solar storage adjacent the heat exchanger. Since these temperatures vary throughout the day, a simple thermostat would not suffice and instead a special Differential Temperature Controller (DTC) is used. Essentially this compares the temperatures obtained by two remote sensors to ensure that sufficient thermal gain is available for pump and transfer losses to be offset by useful collector heat, see Figure 6.3. It also ensures that heat is not left unnecessarily in the collector and that heat is not accidentally pumped out of the cylinder.

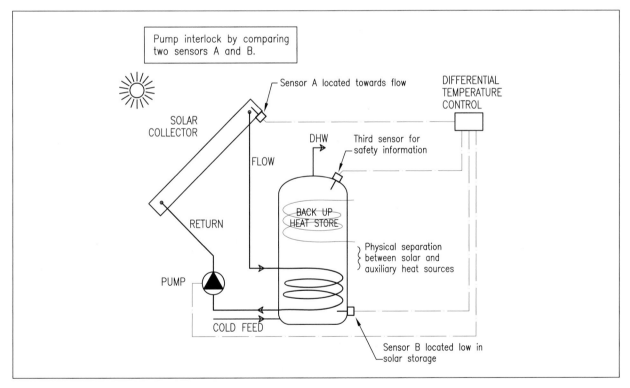

Figure 6.2 The principles of temperature controlled interlock to prevent fossil fuel heat loss into collector circuit

The DTC will use a lamp or other indicator to indicate pump operation and often will show temperatures around the system. It is wired with a power supply, typically mains 230 V ac, which passes through a relay to the pump. Sensors, typically of the platinum resistance or thermistor type, are wired using extra low voltage cables, that is, less than 50 V dc, with a separator in the box between different voltage classes.

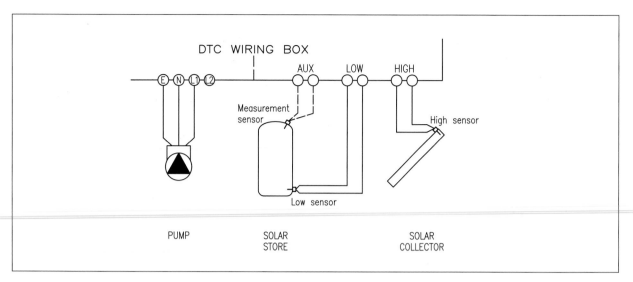

Figure 6.3 Schematic wiring to show the separation of mains voltage and control sensors in a typical differential thermostat controller (DTC)

The principal sensor locations used by the DTC are the collector and the lower part of the solar store. Extra sensors can be added for additional safety information for users or for commissioning purposes, typically one extra is found at the top of the DHW store.

The collector sensor is located preferably inside a purpose-made immersed pocket within the waterways in or adjacent to the flow or highest point in the absorber. Air temperatures, both ambient or inside the collector, should not unduly influence the sensor. A tight fitting gland and a coating of instrument grease or heat transfer paste can help reduce the risk of water ingress and corrosion. The sensor cable must be resistant to the stagnation temperature of the collector, be ultra violet resistant and robust enough to resist vermin attack, particularly from nesting birds.

The solar store sensor is located preferably in a purpose-made immersed pocket within the stored secondary water in or slightly above the return tapping. Ambient temperatures should not be allowed to unduly influence the sensor and a tight fitting gland should secure the sensor from accidental removal. The sensor cable should be well supported around the store. Systems with heat exchangers will use a more sophisticated sensor arrangement.

Sensors for DTCs are required to have good accuracy, +/- 0.1°C, across a wide measurement range of -20°C to 150°C, whilst maintaining a good thermal contact with the fluid being measured. Sensor cables, which typically operate at extra low voltages, should not be run adjacent to cables carrying higher voltages. Where it is necessary for a low voltage cable to cross a high voltage cable it should be done at right angles.

The differential is the difference between switching points or thresholds. In the case of solar DHW systems, this could be collector temperature and primary water store temperature. This differential is adjusted for an individual installation, according to the heat loss of the heat transfer circuit and heat exchanger configuration. A long distance between a collector and store would require a higher differential than a short run.

The hysterisis is the variance around the differential switching point: this can differ according to the direction of movement of temperature, i.e. rising or falling around the switching point and is commonly called the 'dead-band'. It can be adjusted to avoid unnecessary short cycling or hunting of a pump. A typical differential would be between 4°C and 10°C, while the hysterisis would be between 2°C and 5°C. A DTC must essentially have an adjustable differential and at least a fixed hysterisis. The hysterisis is sometimes adjusted using the adjustments of the differential pump on (delta T ON) and pump off (delta T OFF), see Figure 6.4.

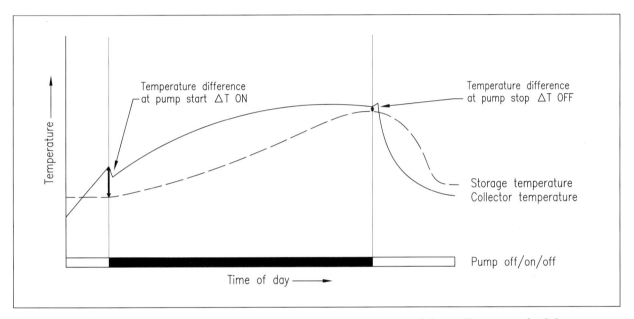

Figure 6.4 The idealised relationship between the temperature of the collector and of the store and operation of the pump assuming constant irradiation through the day

An additional sensor for detecting irradiation levels, i.e. a light sensor, is sometimes used with the two DTC temperature sensors where, for example, there is unfavourable shading across part of the collector or a large collector array where no one point correctly represents the average temperature. This, along with output from the DTC temperature sensors, can optionally provide variable speed control of the circulating pump to maintain a higher efficiency heat transfer at the collector.

During commissioning and periodic maintenance, it is necessary to check the circulation rate of the solar primary circuit fluid in order to confirm that sufficient heat extraction will occur under maximum irradiation. It is also necessary to check that unwanted air is removed from pipework prior to checking fluid levels. As such, checks may take place when available solar irradiation does not create enough circulation, e.g. when there is cloud cover or at night, a suitable method of providing circulation at any time should be available. The DTC should therefore include a manual override to engage circulation for commissioning in all weather conditions, plus a means of accurately indicating the primary circulation rate.

It should not be forgotten that while pump control using DTC can be used to optimise collector performance in relation to irradiation levels, it could also be used to modify the temperature difference, delta T, of the whole collector circuit in relation to the heat exchanger. A heat exchanger requires a sufficient delta T to drive heat across the exchanger boundaries and consideration should be given to the possibility that by the time the flow has reached the solar store, that this might be insufficient. Depending on circulation rates, the delta T between flow and return can range from 10°C to 40°C. Higher flow temperatures, i.e. from lower circulation rates, will result in more heat being lost through the primary pipework. This will, however, enhance stratification in the solar storage.

An important control feature for a fully filled system is the limitation of circulation according to collector temperature. A DTC can be used switch off circulation to avoid excessive temperatures reaching sensitive components lower in the circuit. This can also preserve the life of the antifreeze by allowing liquid to vapourise quickly out of the collector below temperature adjusted at the DTC. However, on a bright day, once engaged this feature can lock-out the circulation until the evening when the temperature drops allowing condensation. See also Appendix C, Sections 5.5, 7.13 and 7.16.

Another form of pump control, previously mentioned, is based on a light sensor often a small photovoltaic module fixed next to the thermal collector. These are particularly useful in combination with temperature sensors where a bypass circuit is used to overcome the standing cold fluid present in long primary pipe runs, see Figure 6.5. Here the light sensor anticipates increasing light levels sufficient to begin pumping the bypass circuit until this is hot enough to satisfy the normal DTC operation. The second pump is then engaged to load the solar store in the normal way but with less risk of losing useful heat out of the store via the return line. Where a light sensor is used without a DTC, or other temperature control, useful heat can be lost from the store or even cause overheating of the secondary circuit. Where multiple collector arrays or stores are used, separate flow meters are advised by each pump, see Section 7.3.3 and 7.3.4.

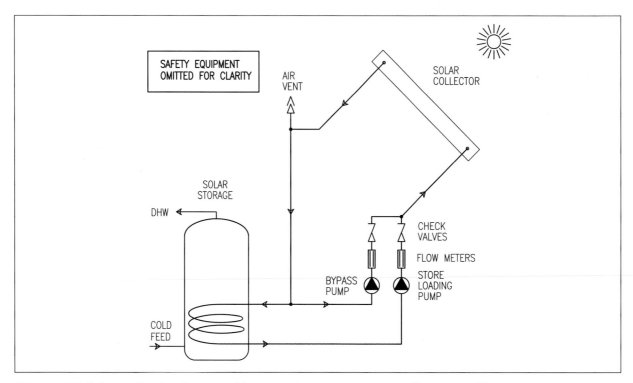

Figure 6.5 Schematic pipe layout of bypass circuit to improve efficiency of long pipe runs

A DTC can also combine additional functions such as: bring on a pump to prevent freezing, record historical temperatures, which is useful for fault finding, provide total pump run hours information, control back-up heating and operate pasteurisation cycles to minimize bacteria growth.

6.1.4 Circulation meters

An indication of the circulation rate in solar primary systems is essential for proper commissioning so as to ensure that there are no air or vapour locks and to set the correct maximum circulation. A purpose-built 'flow' indicator and combined regulator using a clear glass window with a spring-loaded float is often used. Without such a device it is almost impossible to confirm the function of the collector circuit, unless there is strong, direct sunlight at the time of commissioning. Flow indicators are normally fitted on the return line below the check valves, as this is the lowest temperature point on the circuit, see Figure 6.6.

An alternative is to use two thermometers on the flow and return pipes, for example on thermo-siphoning circuits, although these are only useful if there is solar gain during commissioning.

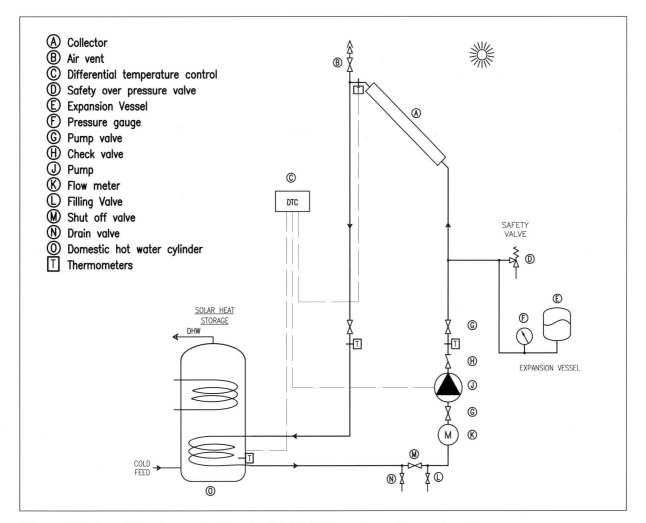

Figure 6.6 Detailed schematic of typical fully filled solar primary circuit layout

6.1.5   Check valves

One-way valves or check valves are used in solar DHW circuits in two scenarios:

● Anti-gravity (anti-buoyancy)

● Circuit diversion

Precautions against unwanted reverse heat flow up from the store at night are important, otherwise useful heat will be lost. When there are clear-skies at night, the collector can fall below ambient temperature, due to the 'black body' radiation effect, and this can drain the solar store of heat gained previously that day. The solution requires at least one, but preferably two, anti-gravity check valves to be fitted, one in the flow and one in the return circulation pipe. Great care must be taken not to accidentally isolate safety valves or expansion vessels and to permit a full drain down, either by extra drain points or by manual de-activation of the valves. A gravity circulation system does not have this problem since the collector is lower than the storage vessel.

Where multiple stores or collectors are used, the primary circuit is likely to be divided with the main circuit diverted to feed relevant branch circuits, see also Sections 7.3.3 and 7.3.4. A check valve paired with a pump is one method of preventing unwanted circulation, or alternatively a motor valve or electro-thermic actuated valve can be used. In each case, the temperature ranges of the solar circuit have to be taken into account. In particular, motorised valves with continuous temperature resistance exceeding 120°C should be specified with short duration capability of over 150°C. Similar consideration should be given to check valves, see further Figures 7.4, 7.5 and 7.6.

6.1.6   Systems allowing full thermostatic control

The most common form of automatic thermostatic control for solar DHW is by use of the limiting thermostat that is built-in to most standard DTCs, see Section 6.1.3 and Appendix C. This 'St max' function is similar to that of a standard bimetal cylinder thermostat except that the sensor and relay are separated and the sensor is more accurate, typically made from platinum. The DTC is usually already electrically connected so that the pump is switched off automatically at an adjustable setting, selected upon commissioning. The pump relay is frequently of the changeover type so it is simple to wire in a second pump or valve if required. In this way, heat can be diverted away from the solar store or to a second store but, at its simplest, the main primary pump is simply switched off. The 'St max' store temperatures would typically be between 60°C and 85°C, dependent on the location of the sensor but also dependent on the whether a target temperature is specifically chosen to reduce secondary water limescale formation.

A second tier of thermostatic control may be specified, particularly in the case of unvented secondary stores. Here, a non self-setting limit thermal cut-out is used. This is not normally built into a DTC and is independently specified. This should act to cut power to the circulation pump, but not to the DTC, as this is required to diagnose information from the sensors and provide users with information to indicate a malfunction. In some circumstances, a motorised valve is required to act as an energy cut-out device activated by a thermostat, particularly where the collector lies wholly or partly below the solar store. Where a motorised valve is not used, it is imperative that further circulation of heat into the store is prevented upon activation of the thermal cut-out, one way being to use separate check valves on both flow and return. No valve can be fitted between the expansion vessel and collector.

It should be noted that solar primary systems with gravity circulation, where the collector is intentionally located below the solar store, do not easily permit full electronic thermostatic control since there is no electric pump and the use of a motorised valve to cease circulation may be required. It is important to ensure that this does not accidentally isolate any other controls.

6.1.7   Motorised valves suitable for solar primary circuits

The stagnation temperature of most modern solar collectors will exceed 150°C under strong sunlight. For short periods, fluid at these high temperatures may circulate in a sealed system and vapour or steam may form, see Section 5.5. This will exceed the temperature limits of many typical motorised valves found on the market. Motorised valves of the correct rating are available and should be specified specifically for solar circuits i.e. those with high temperature limit capability and glycol resistance. In all cases, motorised valves should be located away from the collectors on the coolest part of the circuit, typically on the return line, but without restricting any other safety controls.

6.1.8   Systems without full thermostatic control

Without full thermostatic control, the over-temperature of the secondary pre-heated water, such as with older systems, can otherwise be prevented by:

- The user intervening to run off DHW

- Automatic DHW discharge

- Primary heat diversion

These methods would be wasteful of water and heat and not in keeping with the intentions of the Water (Fittings) Regulations or Part L of the Building Regulations. However, if these are not achieved in a system without full thermostatic control, the result can be uncontrolled solar storage temperatures entering the rest of the DHW circuit. It could also result in the primary temperatures exceeding the design limit or a loss of primary fluid.

In a system designed without full thermostatic control, loss of power to the primary circulation pump and pump control, perhaps due to electrical maintenance or fault, would give rise to a potentially dangerous situation. There is also a serious risk of breaching the requirements of Part G3 of Building Regulations which limits the storage temperature of DHW for volumes over 15 litres.

Full thermostatic control is always preferential compared to reliance on users, water wastage or electrical devices. Designing a system to meet paragraph 4.1.4 of BS EN 12976 and prEN 12977 will mean that a more robust means of secondary water control will be provided.

When no thermostatic control device is installed controlling the solar primary heat input, a temperature relief valve should be fitted to the top of the store with sufficient capacity to prevent storage temperatures reaching or exceeding 100°C. The temperature relief valve must meet BS EN 1490 and be self-setting.

If a solar hot water secondary store has an open vent, the store must be either of the indirect type with a dedicated cold water storage cistern for secondary water, or it should be provided with a non self-setting thermal energy cut-out to control the solar primary circuit in addition to any automatic temperature control.

Rather than stop all primary circulation in the case of an overheat situation, it is possible to divert heat away from the secondary storage to 'heat dumps', such as space heating, swimming pools, fans etc. This can be arranged either with built-in options to differential temperature controllers or by the use of independent thermostats acting on motorised valves or pumps with check valves. Care should be taken that the extra circuits are suitably temperature resistant and that the additional system expansion volume is satisfactorily accommodated. If heat dumps are required to disperse the maximum power of the solar gain, a figure of 0.7 kW /m² collector should be assumed, see further Figures 7.4 and 7.5.

6.2   Expansion and overpressure control

6.2.1   Primary overpressure control

Primary over-pressure control is mainly an issue of safety. If the system pressure is at an incorrect setting or becomes excessively high then there is a possibility that a steam explosion may occur. Historically, excess pressure was dealt with by allowing steam and water to exit from the system through an open safety vent pipe. However, this required user-intervention to confirm or set the system back to the commissioned settings and so does not meet the requirements of paragraph 4.1.4 of BS EN 12976. This standard requires that a system should not require user interaction to return to normal operation and assumes no fluid content leaves the solar primary circuit, even under stagnation conditions. If this requirement is met, the system is termed 'hydraulically secure'. If strong solar irradiation coincides with a loss of circulation power, however temporary, and whether intentional, or by fault, the use of an open vent for controlling over-pressure on a solar primary is inadvisable if only to prevent high vapour loss and condensation risk during the summer.

Where repair or maintenance is required for an existing open vented primary solar system, the open vent safety pipe should be checked for the following characteristics:

- A minimum diameter of 22 mm
- Continuous rise from the point of connection as near to the collector as possible
- No restriction or risk of deformation along the entire route from the collector to its termination
- Discharge below the level of the cover of a feed and expansion cistern

For systems marketed as new where the pressure of any part of a system is foreseeably expected to exceed 0.5 bar, then the requirements of the current Pressure Equipment Regulation are required to be met. Normally, warm water systems up to 110°C are exempt from this Regulation, however, a solar DHW system in the UK will easily exceed this temperature limit and so should not be thought of as exempt on this condition. The threshold pressure of 0.5 bar can be exceeded where the cumulative addition of the overall height of the circuit, the maximum pump head and system pre-charge are added together. The Regulation calls for a minimum of 'sound engineering practice' to be used, but in many cases, particularly if large volumes or high pressures are present, certain extra essential safety requirements must be met as per the Pressure Equipment Regulations. These include consideration of:

- Adequate strength materials

- Experimental design method

- Provisions to ensure safe handling and operation

- Means of examination

- Means of draining and ventilating

- Prevention of corrosion or other chemical attack

- Assemblies

- Protection against exceeding the allowable limits of pressure equipment

- Marking and labelling

- Operating instructions

6.2.2   Safety valves

All safety accessories, including pressure safety valves, are required to meet Category IV of the Pressure Equipment Directive and carry a 'CE' mark where sold separately and traded within the single European market. Certain minimum labelling is required in particular the essential maximum design pressure value 'PS' and the nominal size 'DN'. The design limit temperature 'TS' is also an important variable. These are the values set by the valve manufacturer so that the designer or purchaser of an assembly of components can correctly choose the components. These will correctly protect the system under all foreseeable conditions. Where the system includes a solar collector, the value of 'TS', the highest expected fluid temperature, is carefully selected as to where the valve is located.

Whereas historically, sealed heating systems were considered to operate at a maximum of 3 bar, with solar heating it is often desirable to design systems with equipment designed to a higher termination pressure 'PS' in order to control vaporisation within collectors where they are fitted at high levels, such as on roofs. Values for safety over-pressure valves from 'PS' between 3 and 6 bar and 'TS' 120°C. are now common in the UK for solar systems. For collector arrays of up to 50m² in the UK, safety valve sizes of no less than DN15 are suggested.

Safety over-pressure valves must be located without any closable device or deformable pipe between them and the collector. In this circumstance, whilst it may be instinctive to locate a safety valve adjacent to a solar collector, it should be considered that this is the hottest point of the circuit and usually the least accessible part of the system particularly when considering regular maintenance. An adjacent roof window or a ground-mounted collector may provide reason to accept a safety valve location close to the collector on grounds of ease of access however, consideration to safe termination of released fluids and the durability of safety valve components externally should be carefully considered. Furthermore, in the event of a safety valve releasing fluids where located immediately adjacent to a solar collector, it is most likely that this event will coincide with the collector being under very hot stagnation conditions. Here, the release of fluid is most likely to be superheated vapour that can cause an undesirable erratic, reverberant effect upon discharge. The preferred location for a safety valve is generally nearer to the store where it is more likely to discharge a cooler liquid in a controlled manner.

The termination of the low-level safety valve discharge outlet should be directed to a safe location, similar to that required for safety valves of unvented cylinders or sealed heating systems. Discharge pipes should not reduce in diameter relative to the outlet of the valve and common discharge pipes from different systems are possible on the basis that simultaneous discharge has a low probability.

In the case where antifreeze is used, it may be desirable to use a receptacle to contain the antifreeze for re-use. Such a receptacle should meet or exceed the requirements of BS 4213 especially in respect of temperature rating. It should also be able to contain the contents of the entire primary system above the location of the safety valve and not be sealed from atmosphere, so as to permit the rapid removal of air from the receptacle during release of fluid.

Where a system is designed to be 'hydraulically secure', this implies that a relatively large vessel is already present in the system and that there is no possibility of fluid discharge through the safety valve. Hydraulically secure systems require a calculation of fluid contents and vessel size to be verified as per Annexe D or E. Such systems should place tamperproof caps on filling points to reduce the risk of accidental re-filling beyond the calculated filling levels.

Where any part of the collector array can be isolated, as is sometimes the case on larger systems, localised safety valves must be fitted to each separate array. In this arrangement, an auxiliary safety valve of a lower release limit could be fitted in an accessible position nearer the store. Given the current limitations of non-metallic pipe technology, plastic or rubber pipes or valves should not be used between a solar DHW solar collector and the safety valve or other means of overpressure control.

6.2.3   Primary expansion control

Expansion in the primary circuit occurs from temperature rises within the fluid during normal and fault conditions and is an issue of safety and user convenience. See also Section 2.4. Primary expansion control is mainly an issue of safety and user convenience. If the expansion is not accommodated, it may cause fluid contents to discharge from the system through a safety valve or open vent, thereby requiring re-filling. By designing the hydraulic components of a system to meet paragraph 4.1.4 of BS EN 12976, a system would not require user interaction to return the system back to normal operation. This in turn implies that no fluid shall normally leave the solar primary circuit even under stagnation conditions, see also 6.2.1.

Assuming this is met and the system is designed to be 'hydraulically secure', the use of a header cistern for controlling expansion on a solar primary circuit, would not be possible. A cistern is liable to evaporate fluid rapidly due to the temperatures achieved by advanced collectors. In a sealed system meeting BS EN 12976, the expansion of fluid is accommodated in either a membrane expansion vessel or a drainback vessel containing an air pocket.

6.2.4   Membrane expansion vessels

Where a membrane expansion vessel is used to control expansion, it is not insulated in order to reduce the effect of heat on the flexible rubber membrane. The vessel is not part of the circulatory circuit and is normally designed to remain cool.

Expansion vessels, such as indicated in Figure 6.7, can be considered pressure accessories under the Pressure Equipment Regulations and must carry a 'CE' mark. The marking will also provide information regarding the limit temperature 'TS', nominal size 'DN', limit pressure 'PN' and the nominal volume 'V'. The working or utilisation volume of an expansion vessel will be less than the nominal volume and it is critical that the correct vessel, along with its correct pre-charge pressure, is selected to avoid future problems. Solar expansion vessels are sized to provide a significantly increased volume over those used with traditional sealed heating systems and the typical smallest size would have a nominal volume of 18 litres, see also 7.13.

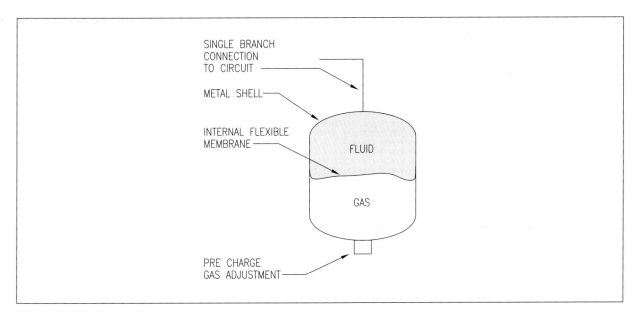

Figure 6.7 Section through a membrane expansion vessel

Ordinary central heating expansion vessels are not normally rated to operate at suitable temperatures found in solar DHW systems, and special vessels for solar would be rated to at least 100°C, or 120°C. They also have to be able to handle glycol antifreeze. These temperatures are still insufficient to withstand the full stagnation temperatures of advanced collectors hence solar expansion vessels should be placed:

- On the return line after the pump

- Orientated with fluid side up, gas side down

- Located far enough away from the collectors to ensure that the utilisation or working volume is less than 50% of that of the fluid between the collector and the vessel

If the latter cannot be met by suitable pipe sizing, an intermediate auxiliary vessel must be used in order to prevent the possibility that steam or vaporised fluid may strike the rubber membrane. An alternative to an auxiliary vessel is to either use a large diameter un-insulated pipe on the expansion vessel branch or proprietary aluminium fins that clip to the branch pipe to assist in cooling, or both. Clear warning labelling and guards may be required where any such heat dispersion equipment is accessible without tools.

Expansion vessels are designed for interior locations only and must be fitted so that the lower surface is accessible to adjust the pre-charge pressure. Where glycol antifreeze is used, compatible anti-corrosion inhibitors must be used to prevent corrosion of the steel used inside.

An expansion vessel adjustable pre-charge is set at a minimum to the equivalent static height of the system i.e. from the top of collector to the vessel. The system pressure is then set to this value plus sufficient over-charge to prevent sub-atmospheric pressure at the top of the circuit that could lead to air ingress or premature boiling. It should be noted that the filling pressure on commissioning is likely to be substantially greater than the system will fall to on the coldest days and therefore a suitable over-pressure is required upon filling. Vessels are normally supplied with a nominal 3 Bar nitrogen gas pre-charge allowing a simple reduction on site using a hand pressure gauge. If the gas has to be recharged, ideally this would be done with a nitrogen bottle, although the use of an air tyre pump is more common, despite the risk of intruding moisture and oxygen into an untreated steel vessel that could corrode. Figure 6.7 shows the adjustment point for the gas pre-charge, where the hand pressure gauge or air tyre pump is temporarily connected to take a reading, but only once the vessel has been disconnected from the system. This will allow a true measure of the existing gas pre-charge which otherwise would be altered by the system. The valve is normally similar to that of a car tyre. Although a simple gate valve could be used for isolation, there is a risk these could be accidentally closed during operation hence these should be specified with a lock shield if used. It is preferable to specify a special dual-spring valve union that incorporates O-rings and valve seats in a way that automatically isolates both the system and the vessel upon disconnection. A small drain valve completes the assembly and in this way future maintenance is simplified.

Certain collectors, such as very high efficiency tube collectors, have features that affect the way the fluid evaporates at stagnation temperatures. For example, there may be an intermediary fluid in the tubes, as with heat-pipe types, or the primary transfer fluid may instead circulate within the tubes. The point at which the primary transfer fluid evaporates is adjustable according to the commissioned settings of the system pressures. Whilst it is possible to use a high filling pressure to permit liquid circulation at times of high temperatures, it is preferable to increase the longevity of the antifreeze by allowing an early evaporation point typically no greater than 130°C, see also Section 5.5. At this point, only a few molecules of gaseous antifreeze remain in the absorber of the collector and the majority of the antifreeze remains as fluid displaced into the expansion vessel away from the hottest parts of the collector. Both the filling pressure of the system and the expansion vessel pre-charge affect this situation, as do the settings on the pump controller. The pump controller should be set such that the pump does not attempt to circulate fluid back into the absorber until the fluid has condensed back into a liquid. By using the methods and tables in later chapters of this guide, it is possible to determine the desired point of evaporation, as shown in Figure 7.2.

6.2.5 Drainback vessel with air pocket

Figure 6.8 shows a typical drainback vessel. It can be seen that the working or utilisation volume at the top will be less than its overall, nominal volume. It is critical that the correct overall vessel and air pocket sizes are selected, to avoid operational problems either by a manufacturer or using this guide. The schematic does not show certain features that could be used such as dip pipes used to reduce noise or a bypass to enhance the siphoning action.

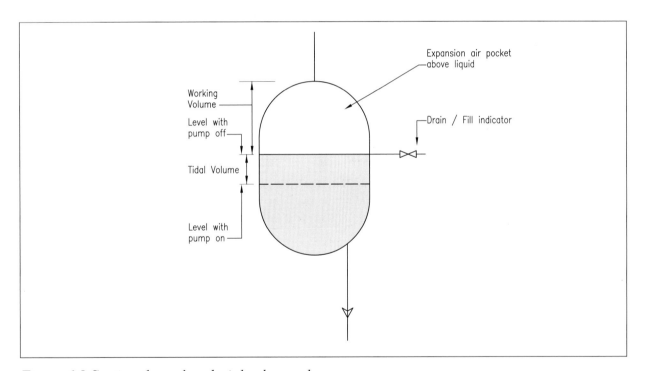

Figure 6.8 Section through a drainback vessel

The operation of a drainback system is shown in Figure 6.9 and Section 3.5. When a drainback vessel is used for controlling expansion in a solar DHW system, it can be considered to be a pressure accessory under the pressure equipment directive, see also Section 6.2.4 . Such a vessel would be expected to carry a 'CE' mark where compliant and traded within the single European market. The limit temperature 'TS', nominal size 'DN', limit pressure 'PN' and the nominal volume 'V' will also be labelled.

As noted in Section 3.5, drainback vessels have no particular equivalent in conventional heating systems and are specific to solar systems. They are frequently sold within kits along with the solar collector. The fluid used in a drainback system can be plain water without antifreeze since in freezing conditions the fluid will have drained away from the collector and into the drainback vessel. Without antifreeze, the drainback vessel itself must be installed in a frost-free location. Optionally antifreeze can be added allowing the vessel to be mounted in the loft above the insulation for example. Consideration should be given to the noise of circulating air and water that is audible during drainback operation depending on the system design.

There are two variants that locate the vessel either in the flow or return pipework. With each choice, there are accompanying bypass or check valve arrangements to 'break' the siphon and permit reliable drainback.

In order to ensure the vessel and drainback system are correctly filled, a simple fill indicator is provided, which spills fluid at the correct height when its valve is open. This limits the fill volume and prevents over-pressuring that must be avoided, as this would reduce the air pocket size. Once filled to the preset operating level, an air pocket is naturally formed in the upper part of the vessel and it is this that creates the means to absorb the operational fluid expansion much like a cushion. When the pump is operating, fluid is pushed up into the collector above and the air is displaced into the drainback vessel causing the fluid level to drop to its 'quiescent' level.

The drainback vessel is sized not only to provide a sufficiently large air pocket to allow for expansion between temperature extremes, but also to provide a sufficient 'tidal' volume of fluid in the bottom to circulate and carry heat away from the collectors. The air in the vessel acts as a cushion in the same way as it or nitrogen does in a membrane vessel hence overall vessel sizing is similar to that for membrane vessels, see detailed

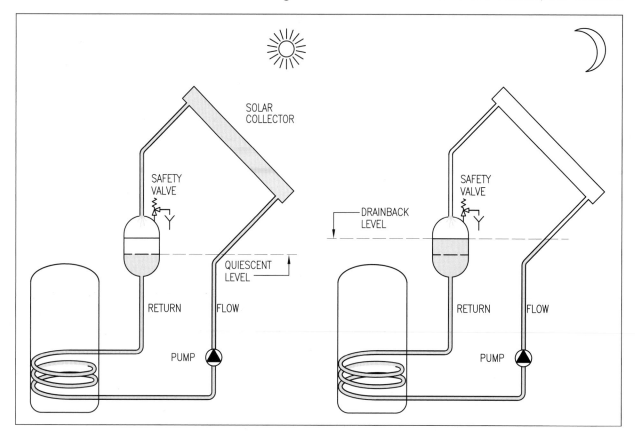

Figure 6.9 Schematic showing operation of drainback

design chapters later in this guide, Section 7.14. There is a lower initial system pressure for drainback systems, typically 0.0 to 0.5 bar. The maximum fluid temperatures can be expected to be lower compared to fully filled systems.

It should be noted that sub-atmospheric pressures are highly likely in drainback systems, either during the siphon-induced drainback or during weather colder than when the system was first filled. This may cause problems with pump cavitation and premature boiling in larger systems or where the pump is located at high levels. The siphon effect occurs once the pump has switched off. Just after the moment that the pump in the drainback system switches off, the columns of fluid in the flow and return pipes almost 'hang' in balance like a rope over a pulley. Providing that one of the pipes terminates in the drainback vessel's air pocket, gravity will cause the fluid to be sucked over through the collector and down into the vessel. During this time, the water columns cause a drop in pressure at the top of the system and this may permit temporary boiling in accordance with the natural behaviour of water, see also Section 7.15.

It is common mistake that drainback vessels are visually confused with membrane vessels and a fitter may attempt to fully fill and pre-pressurise a drainback system erroneously. Should this occur, the air pocket may be accidentally replaced with fluid hence the means of controlling expansion would be lost. Only a safety over-pressure valve would then prevent damage or a possible explosion. Safety relief valves should always be specified with drainback vessels and the vessel must be clearly labelled to warn of the requirements for retaining an air pocket.

6.2.6   Pressure gauge

A pressure gauge, or manometer, is an essential accessory to monitor the system pressure of sealed systems. Even with sealed drainback systems where the initial filling pressure is near zero, a gauge becomes useful to anticipate problems or to safely drain and refill the system. The gauge should be within view of the filling/draining point as well as accessible to the user of the system. Its range would normally be no less than 1-4 bar but 0 - 10 bar is required in some cases for fully filled systems. Drainback systems may require manometers capable of measuring sub atmospheric pressures.

6.3   DHW safety temperature control

6.3.1   Secondary temperature control

Scalding can be considered an increasing risk, especially to children and the infirm, when secondary water temperature rises above 38°C. For most adults exposure to water at 60°C for a few seconds can be hazardous. However, to reduce bacterial growth, distribution temperatures are suggested at no less than 55°C and DHW storage at no less than 60°C. An efficient solar heating system in the UK is easily capable of producing secondary water at scalding temperatures and in some cases, with a proportionally low capacity storage, reaching up to 100°C. If a solar DHW system does not heat the solar store beyond 38°C in the summer months at times when there is no DHW draw-off, then it may be an indication that maintenance or repair is required.

The use of a thermostatic mixing valve, TMV, to reduce the DHW outlet temperatures, is one way to reduce scalding risks. This is done either at or within 450 mm of the point of use of secondary water. The mixing valve should be no less than to the 'Build Cert TMV2' specification and set to no greater than 46°C for a bath as an example. Valves conforming to this specification can maintain temperature stability at all times and will shut down safely in case of cold water failure. A risk assessment would be required to suggest the appropriate target temperature for other outlets and at which appliances or outlets this is required.

It may be considered that a single, centralised TMV located at the start of a DHW distribution system is used for scald protection, such as on top of the DHW store. This is not normally good practice due to the loss of sterilisation of bacteria growth in distribution pipes as well as increased limescale build-up in the TMV. If used, they should be adjusted to provide a mixed water temperature of not less than 55°C and care should be taken to make sure that the DHW draw-off rate is not unduly affected and that safety vents are not obstructed. The effects of limescale should be considered and filters may be required at the inlets to the TMV. Care should also be taken that the cold inlet to the TMV does not remain static for long periods which would increase the risk of bacterial build-up.

Historically, solar DHW systems in the UK and Ireland were not designed to be capable of being thermostatically controlled. During summer, these systems would often suffer excessive DHW temperatures perhaps even boiling through an open vent or discharging through a safety valve. A poignant reminder that the sun is a powerful energy source, not easily 'switched off'.

In more modern times, fitting the hydraulic components of a system which will meet the requirements of Section 4.1.4 of BS EN 12976 i.e. the system is 'hydraulically secure', means that the primary input of solar heat can be simply 'switched off'. Hence, the secondary storage is not required to achieve excessive temperatures nor is user intervention required to return the system back to normal operation. This also means that compliance with the Water (Fittings) Regulation and Building Regulation G3, in England and Wales, is much more straightforward. This in turn means that a system, specified to this standard, will permit full thermostatic control of secondary stored water.

Where the solar primary circuit is not designed with full thermostatic control, it is still necessary to:

- Prevent a solar store over 15 litres from reaching 100°C to comply with the Building Regulation G3 in England and Wales

- Reduce the risk of scalding by storing DHW at a reasonable temperature

7.   Designing the system

7.1   Design overview

The following key design points should be addressed to ensure a safe and reliable solar system:

● Prevention of steam or scalding water from hot water distribution pipes reaching terminal devices to prevent severe scalding risk.

● Freezing of fluid in the solar collector and other parts of the primary circuit where it may damage materials, impede circulation or block safety vents.

● Accumulation of lime-scale, silt and other debris in the solar circuit with loss of circulation, heat transfer, blockage of safety vents or build-up of bacteria.

● Legionella bacteria developing within the consumed drinking or shower water.

● Loss of water quality due to contact with materials and fittings during high stagnation temperatures and pressures.

● Backflow or thermo-siphoning of heated water into a cold water cistern containing wholesome water.

● Disturbance of stratification in the solar storage vessel due to pumps, which increase return temperature at the base of the store causing reduced collector efficiency.

● Loss of dedicated solar storage capacity.

● Loss of the legionella control from back-up heating appliances.

● Overflow or evaporation of fluids from storage cistern.

For a system intended to meet paragraphs 4.3 and 4.4 of BS EN 12976 or paragraphs 6.3 and 6.4 of prEN 12977, the following would also be required:

● The design of the system and the materials of which it is constructed shall be such that there is no possibility of deforming, clogging or lime deposits in its circuits that will drastically influence performance and safety.

● The expansion pipe and the open safety vent pipe shall be connected in such a way that any accumulation of dirt, scale or similar impurities is avoided.

Unless a heat exchanger is fitted between the primary and secondary parts of a solar DHW system, ie. an indirect system, then in addition to the above key design points the installation must also comply with the Water Supply (Water Fittings) Regulations 1999.

To achieve full compliance the system must meet either a European Standard or a European Technical Approval. It may also be subject to the provisions requiring notification of the local Water Undertaking prior to installation.

There is a particular need to ensure that under stagnation conditions a direct system cannot release scalding water or steam from any terminal device.

Design advice for the use of new direct solar thermal systems is not included in this guide. Section 3.2 includes common configurations of direct systems to assist in their identification.

7.2   Example system layouts – key design steps

The most common configuration for a solar DHW system requires that it be integrated with a gas, oil or electric conventional heat source. This is usually accomplished by selection of either a combined store or seperate stores, Section 4.3. This is one of the first strategic decisions to be made in the design process.

Where possible, a single store combining both the solar and DHW backup heater is the preferred choice because:

- The single store has lower surface losses compared to two stores.
- The backup heater thermostat automatically responds to the solar heat without pumps or draw-off.
- The solar heat naturally rises nearest to the draw-off point without pumps or draw-off.
- Bacteria in the solar heated water is naturally sterilised when it passes through the temperature generated by the backup DHW heater.
- The floor footprint is smaller with one store.
- There is one set of safety controls for the stored water.

Two separate stores such as are shown in Figure 4.8, may be required in the case where insufficient height is available for one store. With careful reference to sterilisation of bacteria discussed in Section 5.7, a single store with external backup DHW heater may be chosen.

In deciding on the downstream backup DHW heat source, the integration with the solar system remains vital. With reference to Section 6.1, the following should be considered:

- The appliance must have a thermostatic response to the solar input.
- The appliance will frequently be required to provide all the DHW demand without any solar gains and so must be sized as if the solar system was not present
- The appliance must have manufacturer's approval for safety, durability and reliability when pre-heated by a solar system

Wherever possible, an automatically fuelled DHW backup heater must be wired to provide a thermostatic interlock with the solar storage. Where the appliance is manually fed such as a solid fuel stove, the solar system must provide a readily accessible and accurate

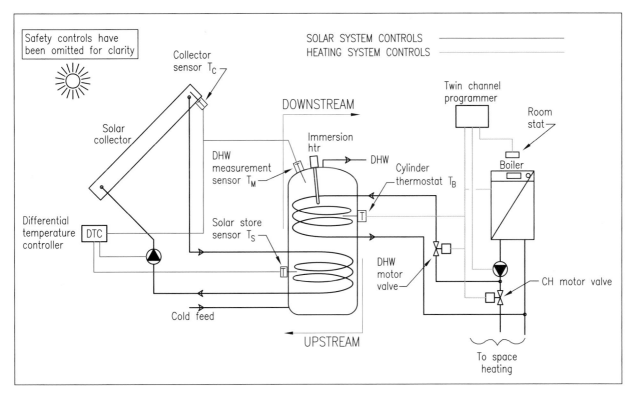

Figure 7.1 Schematic pipework and control layout for integrating an indirect boiler with an indirect solar circuit in a single, combined DHW store.

temperature readout of the solar storage temperature. A DHW backup heater used in summer without any capability of automatic electric control, such as a thermo-syphoning DHW circulator, should only be chosen after carefully considering all other options.

The preferred system layout is shown in Figure 7.1 which will suit the majority of household installations. The solar primary circulation of heat is controlled by the DTC. This compares the sensors Tc and Ts to ensure sufficient thermal gain is available before switching the pump on. Sensor Tm provides safety and monitoring information to the end user. Either Ts or Tm also controls the maximum temperature of the store. Other extra safety controls, not shown in Figure 7.1, may be present according to the type of storage, such as limit thermostats for unvented stores. Figure 7.1 can also represent the functional arrangement when converting an existing combi-boiler where the manufacturer permits the boiler DHW function to be reduced or disabled. Note that some combi-boilers, with integral controls and low voltage contacts, make this conversion unadvisable, see also Section 4.5.

The central heating controls will normally be wholly separate in function to the solar controls. The cylinder thermostat Tb will control the heat delivered from the backup heat source in association commonly with motor valves to provide a fully pumped independent programming between DHW and CH. Note Tb must be located above the lower boiler tapping to respond to both solar and boiler heat. Where the backup heat source is one or more electric immersion elements, these will be located with a thermostat above the solar coil.

Some advanced controls which provide more advanced integration between the two systems are available but are not detailed here.

7.3   Example schematic primary circuit layouts

The heat load of a typical solar circuit can be represented by a solar pre-heat cylinder as indicated in the following schematic layouts, although this can readily be substituted by a combined solar store or a swimming pool. Secondary safety features, primary pump controls and backup DHW heaters are not shown for clarity.

7.3.1   Basic fully filled primary circuit

In a basic fully filled system, Figure 7.2, a differential temperature pump control compares the readings of sensors located in the collector and the store, using this information to control the pump. Check valves, sometimes located in both flow and return, prevent potential heat-loss from unwanted reverse circulation. The highest temperatures can be expected in the flow, hence where a check valve is located here this should not only be resistant to the high temperatures that can be experienced but also designed to be manually held open during flushing procedures. Alternatively, an extra drain point should be located to assist this. The drain and fill point uses three valves to assist removal of air during the filling process. No means of isolation should be placed between the collector and the safety relief valve. The expansion vessel is located in the coolest part of the circuit. This system arrangement is predominant for solar DHW heating, see also Figure 6.6.

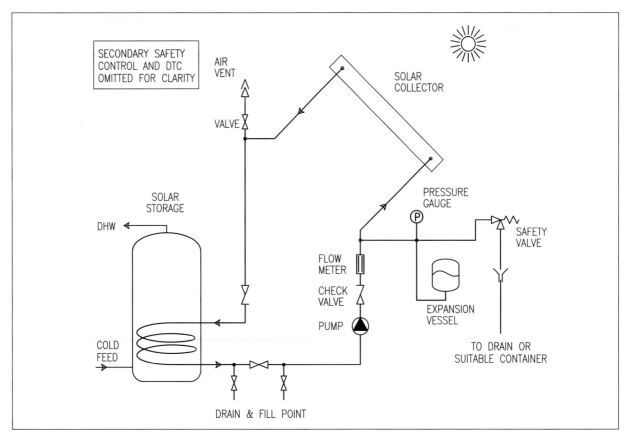

Figure 7.2 Schematic pipework layout of a fully filled solar system with one collector and one heat load (preferred arrangement)

7.3.2 Basic Drainback circuit

In a basic drainback system, Figure 7.3, a differential temperature pump control compares the readings of sensors located in the collector and the store, using this information to control the pump. Unwanted reverse circulation and overheating is prevented by draining back the fluid into a vessel partly containing air. No means of isolation should be placed between the collector and the safety relief valve.

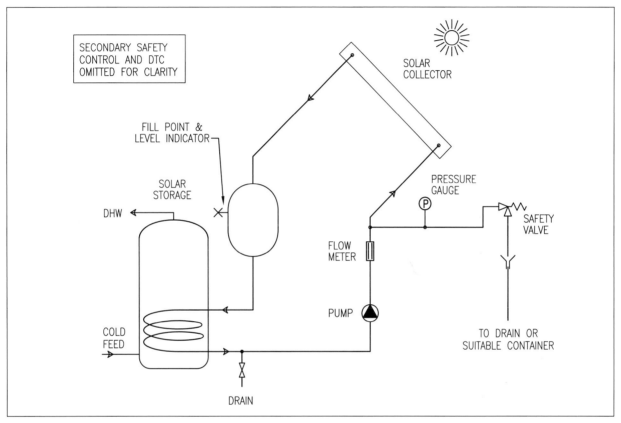

Figure 7.3 Schematic pipework layout of drainback solar system with one collector and one heat load

7.3.3 Multiple heat loads

Using a solar pump controller, either store A or store B in Figures 7.4 and 7.5, can be selected as having the priority from the solar heat, which is advantageous in improving collector efficiency. Once the first store has reached its adjustable target temperature, the second store will be cooler and better able to accept solar loading. Parallel loading, such as where cylinders are doubled up to improve secondary throughput, can be chosen. In this case, care should be taken to balance the circulation through each heat exchanger separately. One of the stores could be a space heating 'heat-dump' radiator for occasional use during high irradiation periods.

A single three-port or two two-port motorised valves can be used instead of a second pump and check valve, however care must be taken to ensure the valves are suitable for the high temperatures in the solar primary. A separate differential pump control is required for each store although this is often built into one DTC box.

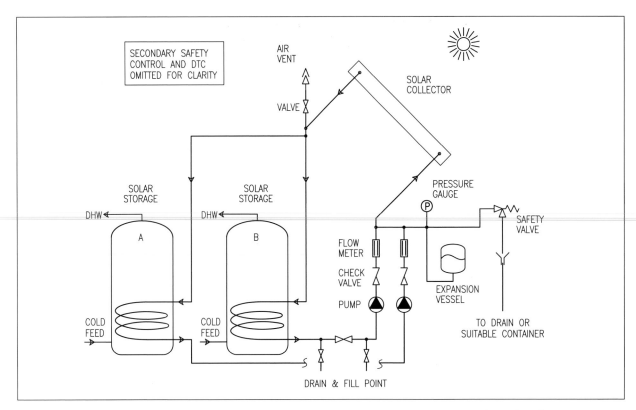

Figure 7.4 Schematic pipework layout of fully filled solar system with two heat loads

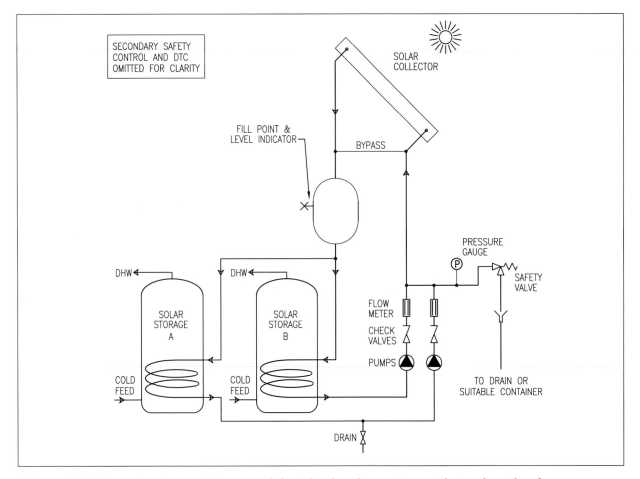

Figure 7.5 Schematic pipework layout of drainback solar system with two heat loads

To use a drainback circuit with any kind of restriction below the drainback vessel requires the use of a small diameter bypass in order to 'break' the siphon and permit the fluid to leave the collector. This must be carefully 'tuned' to a resistance that leaves sufficient circulation round the collector with the pump on and yet large enough to allow drainback.

7.3.4   Multiple collectors

Where a roof has a North/South ridgeline or where there is significant shading over a part of the collector field, it can be desirable to circulate each part of the different collector aspects independently. Here either two or more pumps with check valves can be used or three-port or two-port motorised valves, however care must be taken to ensure the valves are suitable for the high temperatures in the solar primary circuit. A separate differential temperature pump control is required for each collector although this is often built into one DTC box. Figure 7.6 illustrates the arrangement.

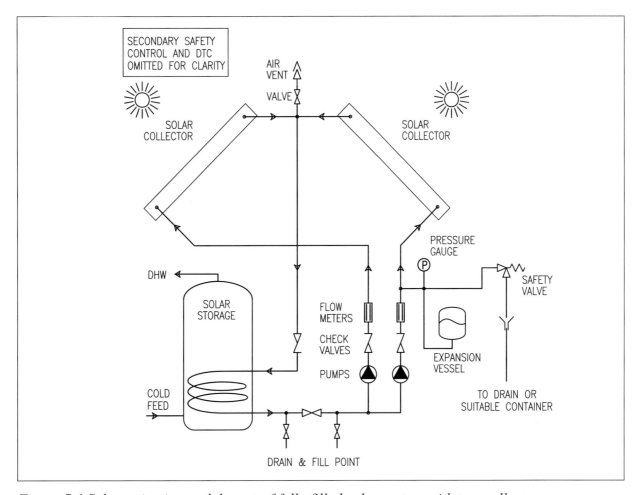

Figure 7.6 Schematic pipework layout of fully filled solar system with two collectors

7.4   Example schematic safety control layout to comply with Building Regulation G3 (England and Wales)

The installation of domestic unvented hot water cylinders is regulated and the following schematic indicates one way to comply with the wording or Regulation G3 for England and Wales.

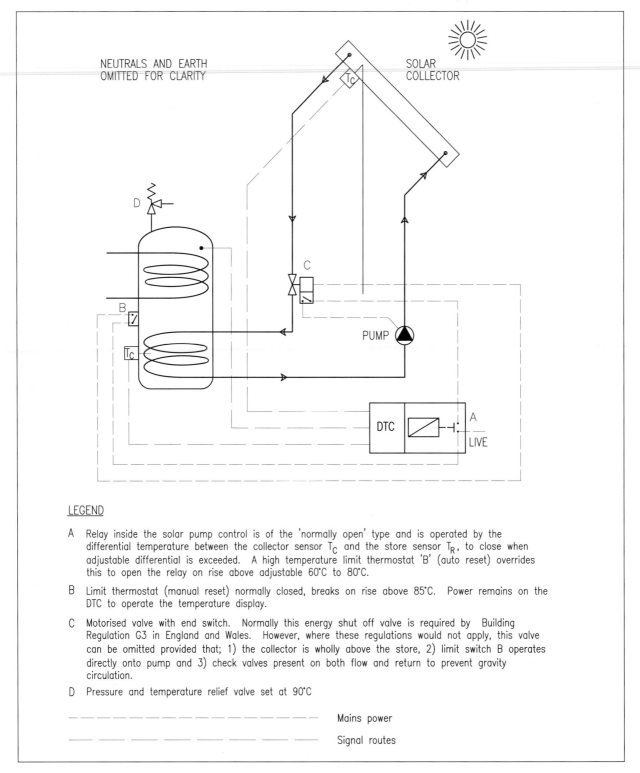

LEGEND

A   Relay inside the solar pump control is of the 'normally open' type and is operated by the differential temperature between the collector sensor T_C and the store sensor T_R, to close when adjustable differential is exceeded.   A high temperature limit thermostat 'B' (auto reset) overrides this to open the relay on rise above adjustable 60°C to 80°C.

B   Limit thermostat (manual reset) normally closed, breaks on rise above 85°C.   Power remains on the DTC to operate the temperature display.

C   Motorised valve with end switch.   Normally this energy shut off valve is required by Building Regulation G3 in England and Wales.   However, where these regulations would not apply, this valve can be omitted provided that; 1) the collector is wholly above the store, 2) limit switch B operates directly onto pump and 3) check valves present on both flow and return to prevent gravity circulation.

D   Pressure and temperature relief valve set at 90°C

——— ——— ——— ——— ——— ——— ———   Mains power

——— ——— ——— ——— ——— ——— ———   Signal routes

Figure 7.7 Schematic layout for solar circuit with unvented DHW store to comply with Building Regulation G3 (England and Wales)

7.5   Overview of system sizing

7.5.1   Collector sizing

1.   Calculate annual DHW load for household
2.   Calculate required DHW energy and allow for system losses
3.   Set a solar fraction of the total DHW energy
4.   Calculate energy to be solar collected
5.   Allow for orientation and shading of collector surface
6.   Choose collector performance and calculate collector area

7.5.2   Storage sizing

1.   Calculate daily DHW load for household
2.   Calculate stored DHW volume (if any)
3.   Calculate dedicated solar pre-heat volume
4.   Add two volumes for combined store size

7.5.3   Store heat exchanger sizing

1.   Calculate collector area
2.   Set circulation rate
3.   Calculate exchange area

7.5.4   Calculating DHW loads

A good assessment of DHW consumption is fundamental to designing a hot water heating system. Typical DHW consumption in the UK is from 30 to 50 litres per day at 55°C per person. These figures can be made more accurate by either a site investigation or by anticipating any proposed DHW using appliances in the design. Special consideration should be given to high flow rate showers, where fitted, due to their strong influence on consumption. Once the DHW consumption is identified in litres per day, it is then possible to calculate the energy required.

The Standard Assessment Procedure for Energy Rating of Dwellings (SAP) provides one method for annual DHW requirements as follows:

Assume:

N	=	Nominal number of people in the house
TFA	=	Total Floor Area (m^2)
V_D	=	Volume of daily consumed DHW
E_{water}	=	Energy content of consumed DHW (kWh)
E_{dist}	=	Energy loss of DHW distribution (kWh)

Hence:

N = 0.035 × TFA - 0.000038 × TFA^2 (if TFA = 420)

Or

N = 8   (if TFA > 420)

The following Table 7.1 provides worked examples based on the SAP formulae:

Floor area	(a) Hot water usage	(b) Energy content of water used	(c) Distribution loss
(m²)	litres/day	kWh/year	kWh/year
30	63	1146	202
40	71	1293	228
50	79	1437	254
60	87	1577	278
70	95	1713	302
80	102	1846	326
90	109	1976	349
100	116	2102	371
110	123	2225	393
120	129	2344	414
130	136	2460	434
140	142	2572	454
150	148	2681	473
160	154	2787	492
170	159	2889	510
180	165	2987	527
190	170	3082	544
200	175	3174	560
210	180	3262	576
220	185	3347	591
230	189	3428	605
240	193	3506	619
250	197	3581	632
260	201	3652	644
270	205	3719	656
280	209	3783	668
290	212	3844	678
300	215	3901	688

Table 7.1 Energy used for domestic hot water taken from SAP 2005

Alternatively, if the temperatures and volumes are known the required DHW energy can be calculated from first principles as follows:

E_{water} = Mass of water x Temperature difference x Specific heat capacity of water

---

Worked example of DHW energy requirements from first principles:

For a household of three people, the daily DHW (Vd) was found to be: **120 litres/day**

Incoming cold water temperature was found to be: **10°C**

Temperature of DHW as drawn off: **55°C**

Converting volume of water (Vd) at 50°C. to mass (Md):

Assume: $Md = Vd \times 0.988$ kg/litre

Hence: $Md = 120 \times 0.988 = $ **119 kg**

Assume: Specific heat capacity of water = 1.16 Wh/kg. °C

Hence: $E_{water} = 119 \times (55 - 10) \times 1.16$

Hence: $E_{water} = 6.21$ kWh/day

Hence: $E_{water} = 2267$ kWh/annum

Hot water is consumed at various temperatures, often mixed either manually at the tap or automatically. This can mean a large amount of water at a lower temperature is used which would have the same energy content as a smaller amount of water at a higher temperature. The conversion formulae between the two is as follows:

Assume:

$V_{d\,New}$ = Volume of DHW at new temperature

$V_{d\,Old}$ = Volume of DHW at old temperature

$T_{d\,New}$ = Temperature of new DHW

$T_{d\,Old}$ = Temperature of old DHW

$T_{d\,Cold}$ = Temperature of incoming cold water

Hence:

$$V_{d\,New} = \frac{(T_{d\,Old} - T_{d\,Cold}) \times V_{d\,Old}}{(T_{d\,New} - T_{d\,Cold})}$$

Taking the above example where the calculation was first made at 55°C and it is required to know the result at $T_{d\,New} = 45$°C then:

Hence $V_{d\,New}$ = ((55 - 10) / (45-10)) x 120 = 154 litres

7.5.5 Heat circuit and storage losses

All heating systems have losses, which, if not taken into account, would lead to undersizing in the design of the system. It is equally valid to anticipate such losses in a solar system when calculating the size of the collector. For example:

- A solar primary pipe circuit that is not insulated will lose the equivalent heat of 45% of the annual yield of the collector. Where reasonably insulated it will lose the equivalent heat of 20 % of the annual yield of the collector. (Similar to over one m² of typical collector area)

- A poorly insulated DHW store can be expected to lose over 3 kWh per day, which in a year, can amount to as much as the solar system can contribute. When reasonably well insulated, the store will lose the equivalent of 25% of the annual yield of the collector. (Similar to over one m² of typical collector area)

Relevant Building Regulations require reasonable measures to minimise these losses (over and above the obvious economic imperative).

For the calculation of heat losses from the solar primary circuit, it should be considered that the pipes will only be hot an average for a few hours per day. During cold weather, the ambient temperature will be lower and the heat loss would be greater, particularly for external pipes. Throughout the day, the temperature in the pipes will constantly vary hence a simplified calculation is suggested as follows.

General rules of thumb for solar pipe losses

Assumes:

Total solar circuit length 20 metres

2000 operating hours annum

Thermal conductivity of insulation = 0.04 W/mK

Insulation wall thickness 18mm.

Ambient temperature 20°C

Pipe temperature 50°C.

Hence:

Heat loss for un-insulated 15mm copper tube = 10.0 W/ per metre run

Heat loss for un-insulated 22mm copper tube = 15.0 W/ per metre run

Heat loss for 15mm. copper tube insulated   = 4.6 W/ per metre run

Heat loss for 22mm. copper tube insulated   = 5.8 W/ per metre run

The above heat loss rates are multiplied by the total circuit length and number of hours to obtain the total energy loss:

Worked examples for insulated 22 mm pipe the loss

= 5.8 x 20 x 2000

= 232 kWh annum

General rules of thumb for solar store losses

The heat loss of a store in kWh/day can be calculated on the basis of SAP. To obtain the loss rate, three factors are derived and multiplied together as follows:

Assume:

Heat loss from solar store	$= Q_{st}$
Volume of solar storage (litres)	$= V_s$
Loss factor	$= L_{fac}$
Volume factor	$= V_{fac}$
Temperature factor	$= T_{fac}$

Then:

$$Q_{st} = V_s \times (L_{fac} \times V_{fac} \times T_{fac})$$

These factors are derived from the individual boxes shown below. Pre-worked example now follows:

Assume:

Insulation thickness (t)	$= 50$ mm
Solar pre-heat storage (V_s)	$= 100$ litres

Then:

$$Q_{st} = V_s (L_{fac} \times V_{fac} \times T_{fac})$$

$$Q_{st} = 100 \times (0.0152 \times 1.063 \times 0.5)$$

$$Q_{st} = 0.808 \text{ kWh per day}$$

$$Q_{st} = 808 \text{ Watt hours per day}$$

$$Q_{st} = 295 \text{ kWh per year}$$

To this figure could be added a further allowance to the heat loss from poorly insulated fittings on the store. These can include immersion bosses and coil tappings that can amount to a loss rate of 100 Watts hence an additional 50 kWh per annum.

The calculation of hot water store losses for the purposes of solar sizing should be considered primarily to be concerned with the losses incurred from the solar storage, rather than the losses from DHW storage fed from a boiler or immersion heater. In a combined store, with solar and boiler heated water in one vessel, the loss from the lower part of the store is used. It should be considered that the solar storage would generally

The store heat loss factor – L_{fac}

This may be calculated for cylinder insulation thickness of 't' mm as follows:

$$L_{fac} = 0.005 + 0.55/(t + 4.0)$$

Pre-worked examples are given in the Table 7.2 below:

Insulation thickness mm.	Cylinder loss factor (L) kWh/litre/day
0	0.1425
12	0.0394
25	0.0240
35	0.0191
38	0.0181
50	0.0152
80	0.0115
120	0.0094
160	0.0084

Table 7.2 Examples of store heat loss factors for varying insulation thicknesses

be at a lower temperature average for the year than any boiler heated storage. It should also be considered that the principal loss from any store will be in the upper region due to stratification and that the temperature will vary throughout the day and year.

The volume factor – V$_{fac}$

This may be calculated for solar storage volume V$_s$ as follows:

$$V_{fac} = (120 / V_s)^{1/3}$$

Pre-worked examples are given in the Table 7.3 below:

Volume (V$_s$)	Volume Factor (V$_{fac}$)
40	1.442
60	1.259
80	1.145
100	1.063
120	1.00
140	0.950
160	0.908
180	0.874
200	0.843
220	0.817
240	0.794
260	0.773
280	0.754

Table 7.3 Examples of store volume factors for varying volumes

The temperature factor – T$_{fac}$

in all cases T$_{fac}$ = 0.5

7.5.6   Solar fraction vs. system efficiency

Once the total energy for a DHW heating system has been calculated, the next decision of the designer will be what proportion of this total will the solar system provide. This proportion is termed the solar fraction and it is the energy supplied by the solar system into the store divided by the total system load. Boiler inefficiencies are not counted within the total load. The figure should be stated in association with the relevant target temperature of the DHW, normally 60°C. At lower target temperatures, the solar fraction becomes 'artificially' higher because not only does the efficiency of the solar collector becomes higher and there are fewer losses in the primary system, but also the target temperature is achieved more regularly. Typical solar fraction figures for the UK vary between 35% and 60% at 60°C.

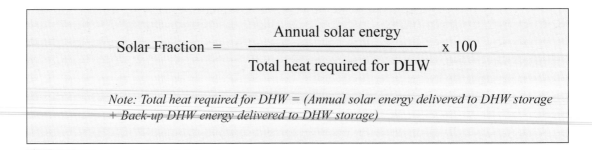

A solar fraction can be specified for an individual month. For example in July the designer could select 90% solar fraction at 60°C. Thereafter the rest of the year would have correspondingly less solar fraction in each month. In this scenario, the overall annual figure would be nominally 58%, according to UK irradiation figures for Southern England. This is indicated in Figure 7.8.

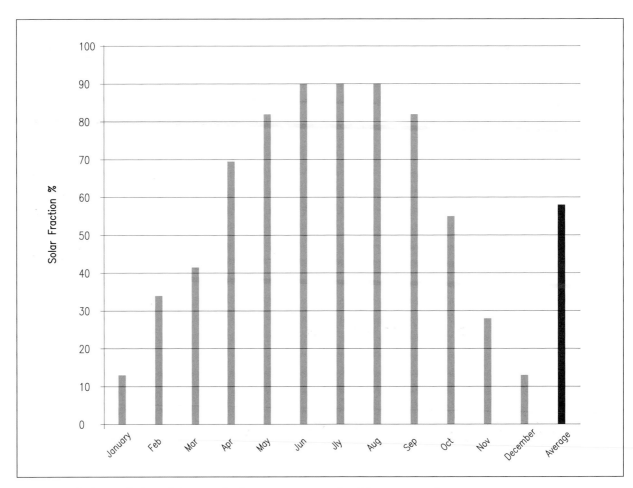

Figure 7.8 Annual distribution of solar energy supplied by a typical system

Attempting to increase the annual solar fraction beyond 60% or for the summer months up to 100% can result in excess heat being generated during peak sunny days requiring careful consideration of the system layout to withstand regular stagnation temperatures and potential overheating in the store. See also Figure 5.2.

The system efficiency is the ratio of useful solar heat to the solar irradiance received at the collector absorber. Useful solar heat gained by the system could be considered to be the amount available where the solar system delivers its heat at the point of DHW distribution, i.e. without secondary pipe losses, but care should be taken when comparing with other data from different systems in case of inconsistencies on this point.

$$\text{System efficiency} = \frac{\text{Useful solar energy delivered to cylinder} \times 100}{\text{Annual solar irradiance in plane of collector} \times \text{Collector absorber area}}$$

The system efficiency is inversely related to the solar fraction in that a system with a high solar fraction tends to have low system efficiency. This is because increasing the collector area will result in periods when there is an excess of generated heat and the losses increase with temperature. System efficiencies in the UK range between 15% and 50%, although 33% could be considered typical. In general, small systems in the UK are designed to optimise the solar fraction and system efficiency is an indicator only used in larger systems were the cost of solar heat is required to be minimised. It can however also by used to roughly size a solar collector see Section 7.6.4.

It is worth noting that there is a third possible analysis of solar efficiency called the fractional energy saving. This is a somewhat fairer analysis than the more commonly quoted solar fraction since it allows for the inefficiency of the back-up heat source and the storage losses. The previously detailed solar fraction analysis tends to become reduced should the back-up system inefficiency increase and so poorly represents the characteristics of the solar circuit. The following text box indicates the fractional energy calculation.

Assuming:

Total heat for DHW without solar at point of distribution = $Q_{\text{Conventional}}$

Back-up heat for DHW after solar at point of distribution = $Q_{\text{Back-up}}$

Then:

$$\text{Fractional energy saving} = \frac{Q_{\text{Conventional}} - Q_{\text{Back-up}}}{Q_{\text{Conventional}}}$$

7.6   Collector sizing

7.6.1   Collector performance

When a collector is tested for performance to BS EN 12975, see also Section 4.2.2, a number of important characteristics are presented which in turn permit the expected annual energy output to be anticipated. Although this process can be quickly analysed with commercial software, manual calculation methods for annual solar energy contribution are provided in the following sections of this guide. These will first require an understanding of the relevant collector characteristics as shown below in the following Table 7.4.

Symbol	Definition	Units	Description
η	Collector efficiency	%	Ratio of energy removed by transfer fluid to incident solar radiation. High values are an advantage.
η_0	Collector efficiency at zero loss or optical collector efficiency.	%	Degree of efficiency when the average collector fluid equals the average ambient temperature. High values are an advantage.
a_1	Basic heat transmittance	$W/(m^2K)$	Not affected by temperature. Low values are an advantage. When added to a_2 at ambient, becomes a simple collector U-value.
a_2	Complex heat transmittance	$W/(m^2K)$	Affected by the square of the temperature. Low values are an advantage.
C	Thermal capacity or thermal inertia	$kJ/(m^2K)$	The quantity of heat required to raise the absorber by one degree temperature. A low value is of advantage in cloudy conditions.
Φ	Angle Incidence modifier	%	Gives the extent of change of efficiency with non-perpendicular light striking the collector. A high value is an advantage particularly in Northern attitudes. Ideally the indirect and direct light components should be stated
G	Solar irradiance	W/m^2	A measure of the strength or power of the sun's energy as it strikes the earth. Usually stated as a horizontal area.
A_g	Gross area	m^2	Maximum projected area of complete collector excluding any integral mounting brackets and pipework
A_A	Net absorber area	m^2	Maximum projected area of an area reached by solar radiation. In tubes with curved surfaces, this area is the projection measured below.
A_a	Aperture area	m^2	Opening through which un-concentrated solar radiation is admitted. Often similar to A_A but discounts any shaded absorber. In tubes with reflectors, this area is the projection measured below.

Table 7.4 Solar collector characteristics

Some typical values of performance according to aperture area are shown in below in the following Table 7.5. This includes a conversion factor if only the gross, or overall, collector dimensions are known, see also 4.1.4.

Collector type	η_0	a_1	a_2	$\Phi @ 50°$	C	Default ratio of aperture to gross area
Evacuated tube	0.60 - 0.85	1.2 - 3.0	0.004 - 0.009	0.84 - 0.95	3 - 50	0.72
Flat plate glazed	0.75 - 0.83	3.0 - 6.0	0.006 - 0.020	0.88 - 0.95	3 - 50	0.90
Unglazed	0.905 +	20 +	0.040 +	0.97 - 1.00	3 - 50	1.00

Table 7.5 Typical values of collector performance according to aperture area

It is especially important to ensure that when comparing collector test results, the same amounts of irradiance, temperature difference and area are used. Although it is attractive to only use one parameter to compare collectors, it should be emphasised that the overall performance is a result of a complex relationship between all the parameters. Furthermore, even a high performance collector can be constrained to poor overall efficiency if the adjoining system components are not matched in performance. Two simple collector performance indicators can be readily calculated as below.

Rules of thumb for collector performance

Collector No.1: η_0 = 0.84 %, a_1 = 2.02 W/(m² x °C), A_a = 2.154 m²

Collector No.2: η_0 = 0.71 %, a_1 = 3.95 W/(m² x °C), A_a = 2.013 m²

Comparisons of 'Effective' collector area A' = η_0 x A_a

Collector No.1: A'= 0.84 x 2.154 = 1.81 m²

Collector No. 2: A'= 0.71 x 2.013 = 1.43 m²

Hence, collector no. 1 gives 20% more 'effective' collector area.

Comparisons of basic collector performance to SAP 2005

= 0.87 - 0.034 (a_1/ η_0) + 0.0006 (a_1/ η_0)²

Collector No. 1: 0.87 - 0.034 (2.01/0.84) + 0.0006 (2.01/0.84)² = 0.792

Collector No. 2: 0.87 - 0.034 (0.71/3.95) + 0.0006 (0.71/3.95)² = 0.699

Hence according to the Table 7.6 below;

Collector No. 1 is medium performance

Collector No. 2 is low performance

Technology Class	Range of SAP collector performance factor
High performance	Above 0.8
Medium performance	Between 0.7 and 0.8
Low performance	Below 0.7

Table 7.6 Classification of collector performance using SAP calculation

A fuller visual appreciation of a collector's response at different operating temperatures can be made using an efficiency graph provided in a typical BS EN 12975 performance report. An example for a single collector is shown below in Figure 7.9 and in Figure 4.4 for different efficiencies and irradiation.

It can be noted that the response line is not quite straight, due to the effect of the quadratic U-value, because the effect of insulation and glazing changes according to temperature. By extending the line to the x-axis, it is possible to anticipate the final stagnation temperature of the collector, noting that the ambient temperature on a hot day is added on. Hence, in the example of Figure 7.9 below, the stagnation temperature would be 130°C + 30°C = 160°C. The line of the graph can be derived from the equation as follows:

Collector Efficiency (η) = η_o - a_1 x ($\Delta T/G$) - a_2 x ($\Delta T^2/G$)

Where:

η_o =   Collector efficiency measured at zero heat loss

ΔT =   Temperature difference between ambient and the average of the collector absorber.

a_1 =   Heat loss coefficient at zero heat loss

a_2 =   Temperature dependence of the heat loss coefficient

G =   Hemispherical solar irradiance

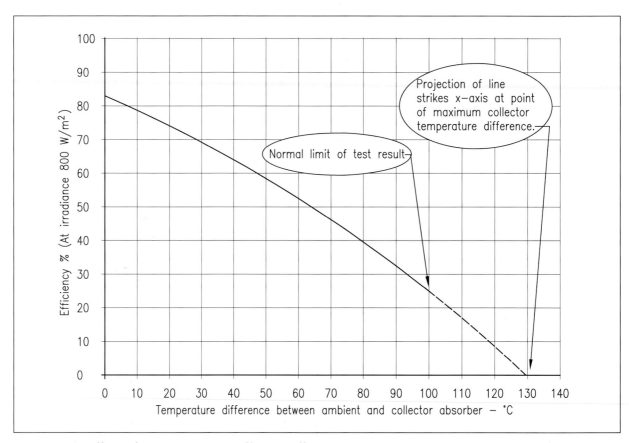

Figure 7.9 Effect of instantaneous collector efficiency against average temperature of the absorber

7.6.2   UK irradiation map

Collector sizing is strongly influenced by the solar irradiation that will enter the solar collector. This in turn is affected throughout the UK by the latitude and average cloud cover. It should be particularly emphasised that the difference between the north of Scotland compared to the tip of Cornwall is greater than 25% and this can be expected to be reflected in the respective collector areas where equivalent performance is expected. The map shown in Figure 7.10 gives an illustration of the variance of annual solar energy striking the ground that can be expected and hence an absolute or relative weighting can be derived.

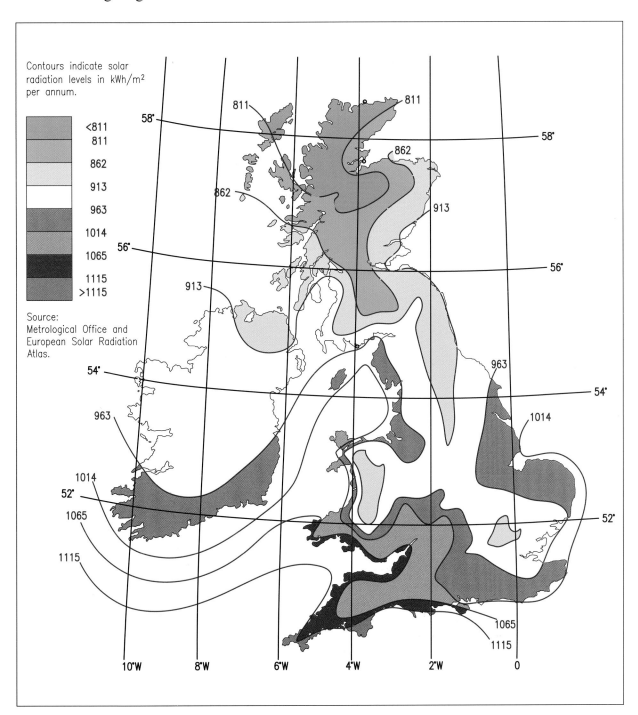

Figure 7.10 British Isles irradiation map

7.6.3   Collector sizing rules of thumb

On the basis of the assumptions indicated below, the collector area sizing for central UK and Ireland can be quickly estimated as a rule of thumb in Figure 7.11. By also using the irradiation map in Figure 7.10, the data can be approximately weighted to each region. Where doubt exists, the alternative and more accurate calculation methods of Section 7.6.5 should be considered. Where complex circuits, non-DHW loads or detailed time period analysis is required, then proprietary simulation software is likely to be required.

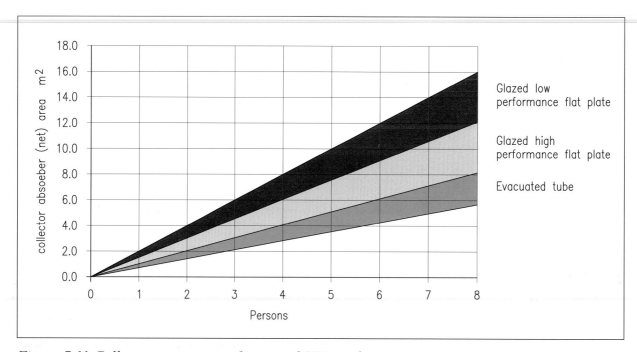

Figure 7.11 Collector sizing ratios for typical UK conditions

The following assumptions are made when using Figure 7.11 for collector sizing:

- The daily hot water use is between 30 - 50 litres at 55°C.

- Desired solar fraction 40% - 50% at 60°C.

- Collector orientated between SE and SW

- Collector pitched between 30° and 55°

- Little or no shading on collector

- Primary pipework insulation greater than 15 mm wall thickness

- Cylinder insulation greater than 35 mm. wall thickness

- Primary circulation temperature is differential controlled

- Dedicated solar storage adequate i.e. $V_s/V_d > 0.8$

- Heat exchanger area in store is adequate i.e. 0.3 m² per collector absorber m²

Worked example

For 3 people in central UK, using 120 litres of DHW consumed at 55°C, the approximate collector absorber (net) area would be:

Glazed flat plate low performance   = 4.5 - 6.0 m²

Glazed flat plate high performance = 3.0 - 4.5 m²

Evacuated tube   = 2.1 - 3.0 m²

With all collector sizing methods, a consideration should be given to shading by multiplying nominal collector areas by the factors indicated in Table 5.2. Once all calculations are done, in practice, the nearest commercially available size is chosen.

7.6.4   Collector sizing method 2

An alternative calculation can be made as below once the steps detailed in Section 7.5.1 have been completed. A worked example is indicated below based on the data shown in Table 7.7.

Example Energy load	Energy annum kWh
DHW usage 120 litres per day	2267
Solar pipe losses	232
Solar store losses	295
Store losses from tappings	50
Total DHW load annum	2844
Solar Faction at 60°C	40%
Solar energy target to collect if optimum	1138

Table 7.7 Example solar energy target for worked example of collector sizing

Reference should be now made to Section 5.3 to establish the proportional loss due to an unfavourable pitch, orientation or shading. The relevant factors are then applied to the desired solar energy target taken from Table 7.7 and calculated as shown below.

Worked example

Solar energy target to collect if optimum = 1138 kWh per annum

For a South-West facing roof pitch at 70°, the irradiation loss is 15 %

Hence the solar energy to collect = 1138 x 115% = 1309 kWh

With reference to Section 7.5.6, the overall system efficiency can be assumed and applied with the solar fraction to the annual solar irradiation and the worked example is continued as shown below.

Worked example for typical performance collector

Assume:

Target energy to collect annum	= 1309 kWh
Average system efficiency	= 33 %
Average Home Counties annual irradiation	= 1000 kWh/m²

$$\text{Collector absorber (net) area} = \frac{\text{Target energy}}{\text{Annual irradiation} \times \text{System efficiency}}$$

Hence:

Collector absorber (net) area	= 1309 / (1000 x 0.33)
	= 4.0 m²

7.6.5   Collector sizing method 3

A more accurate calculation of the required collector area can be made once the overall desired solar energy gain at the collector is identified. This quantity is entered on the vertical axis of the Figure 7.12 after normalisation i.e. to a fixed daily consumption of 100 litres per day of DHW at 55°C. This allows the collector area and collector efficiency to be derived from the horizontal axis.

Worked example

To use Figure 7.12, the solar energy collection target is first adjusted assume 100 litres consumption per day. Assuming the energy was originally calculated for 120 litres consumption already shown in table 7.7:

Hence normalised energy   = 1309 kWh x 100/120

                                     = 1091 kWh

From graph:

The net collector area rate at 100 litres day for a typical performance collector is = 3.4 m²

The net collector area rate at 100 litres day for a high performance collector is = 2.1 m²

For 120 litres draw off, the above areas are increased in proportion by a factor of 120/100 = 1.2

Hence

The net collector area for a typical performance collector is = 4.0 m²

The net collector area for a high performance collector is = 2.5 m²

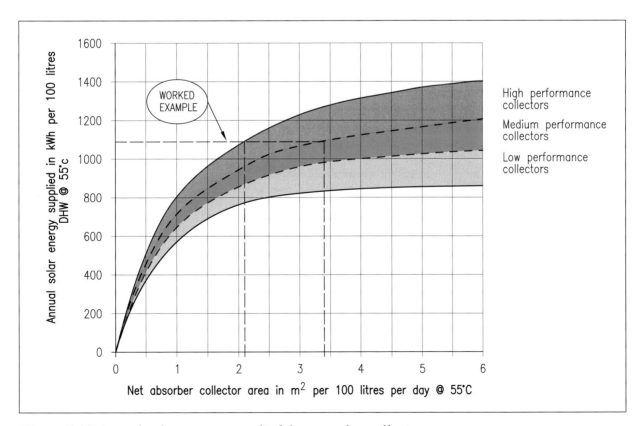

Figure 7.12 Annual solar energy supplied from a solar collector

7.7   Solar storage sizing

7.7.1   Solar storage performance

The design of the solar storage strongly affects the performance of the whole solar system, principally by its temperature and the corresponding lower temperature achieved at the return line to the collector. The lower the return temperature, the higher the collector's efficiency will be. Hence, the factors to be considered are the size of solar storage and stratification, see Section 4.4.

The calculation of heat loss of solar stores is analysed in Sections 5.9 and 7.5.5. Solar storage can also be tested for performance according to prEN 12977-3 by an approved test house and commercial software used for simulation. Where such test results are not available then a manual calculation method is provided in the following sections of this guide. These will require an understanding of the relevant store definitions as shown below and in Figure 7.13.

Dedicated solar storage implies that no other heating source can normally heat the solar pre-heat volume. Normally heated includes any heat source intended to meet the mean daily domestic hot water demand. Normal heat does not include sources controlled by manual operation for occasional boost beyond mean daily domestic hot water demand or automatic cleansing routines additional to those intended to meet the mean daily domestic hot water demand.

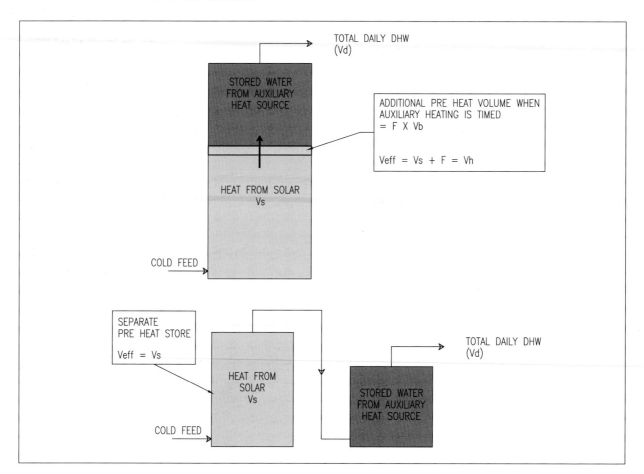

Figure 7.13 The interaction of solar and back-up heated stored water

V_s	=	Volume of storage dedicated to the solar system (litres)
V_d	=	Volume of daily consumed DHW (litres)
V_b	=	Volume of standby or stored heat from back-up heat sources (litres)
V_{eff}	=	Effective solar volume (litres)
V_{total}	=	Total volume of combined storage (litres)
F	=	Factor of stored water available in a combined cylinder for solar storage

Where the dedicated pre-heat storage (V_s) is combined into a DHW store with the standby stored heat (V_b), i.e. a combined store, then V_s shall be measured below the bottom of the lowest back-up element (electric immersion or heat exchanger coil) down to the lowest element of the solar primary.

The effective solar volume (V_{eff}) is equal to the dedicated pre-heat storage (V_s) only in the case of a separate pre-heat store. In the case of a combined store with a common twice-daily timer, the effective solar volume (V_{eff}) is equal to the dedicated solar storage (V_s) plus a factor times the volume of the remainder of the cylinder (V_b). The correct factor for other types of back-up heat is shown below in Table 7.8.

Type of back-up heat	Factor (F) of back-up storage accessible for solar storage in a combined cylinder
Permanently switched on and thermal stores	Less than 0.1
Overnight (Off-peak)	0.3
Timed twice daily	0.3
Emergency or hygienic de-stratification	0.7

Table 7.8 Proportion of back-up storage available to solar in a combined cylinder

In the case of instantaneous heat sources such as combi-boilers, the volume of standby or stored heat may be zero. In the case of thermal stores, the high storage temperatures require the factor to be treated as for permanently switched on heat sources.

Where a single store has multiple heat sources, and one source is seasonally intermittent, then the value of dedicated solar storage can be calculated from the back-up heat source that is normally used in summer. For example a log-fuelled batch-fed central heating system, which is normally shut-down for the summer, could allow for V_s from below an electric immersion rather than the boiler coil. This is particularly the case during the summer season when the value of dedicated storage volume is most important.

7.7.2   Solar storage according to collector size

In Section 7.6, a rule-of-thumb method of collector sizing was given. A similar method is available for the solar storage size and is shown with the following additional considerations to be taken into account to reduce the chances of scalding and maintain acceptable system performance:

Collector type	V_{eff} - litres storage/net collector are m²
Glazed flat plate low performance	25 - 35
Glazed flat plate high performance	30 - 45
Evacuated tube	40 - 60

Table 7.9 Rates of storage according to collector type

- Where a separate pre-heat cylinder is used, $V_{eff} = V_s$ and should be no less than 115 litres in all cases.

- Where a combined cylinder is used, $V_{eff} = V_s + F (V_{total} - V_s)$ and V_{total} should not be less than 140 litres. Factor F is taken from Table 7.8.

- With a thermal DHW store, larger sizes should always be chosen due to the associated reduced stratification and higher DHW storage temperautres. Special attention should be given to this when further pumped circuits are connected to the thermal store without heat exchangers, due to their strong effect on de-stratification. See also Section 4.4.

- Where a thermal DHW store is also combined with high temperature emitter circuits, only the very highest storage rates should be considered along with additional stratification measures such as internal baffles to limit unwanted mixing inside the store. The greatest care must be taken to design the return pipe to the solar collector so that it is connected at the coolest part of the store.

Two worked examples are shown below.

First Solar Storage worked example

A net area of **4.0 m²** of low performance collector is specified.

If a **separate pre-heat vessel** is to be used:

The smallest volume of V_{eff} is calculated to be: 4 x 25 = 100 litres but this is below the lowest threshold hence the lowest size chosen is **115 litres.**

The larger volume of V_{eff} is calculated to be: 4 x 35 = **140 litres.**

If a cylinder that **combines solar and back-up heat** is to be used:

The smallest volume of V_{eff} is calculated to be: 4 x 25 = 100 litres. This is located below a standby volume (V_b) given to be 95 litres. A timer switching twice a day controls the standby volume hence from table 4.3 the storage factor available to the solar is F = 0.3.

Hence the extra volume available to the solar = 0.3 x 95 = 28.5 litres.

Hence the dedicated solar storage V_s = 100 - 28.5 = 71.5 litres

Hence the overall size of the store (V_{total}) = V_s + V_b = 71.5 + 95

= 166.5 litres.

The larger volume of V_{eff} is calculated to be: 4 x 35 = 140 litres.

Hence the extra volume available to the solar = 0.3 x 95 = 28.5 litres.

Hence the dedicated solar storage V_s = 140 - 28.5 = 111.5 litres

Hence the overall size of the store (V_{total}) = V_s + V_b = 111.5 + 95

= 206.5 litres.

Second Solar Storage worked example

A net area of **2.5 m²** of evacuated tube collector is specified.

If a **separate pre-heat vessel** is to be used:

The smallest volume of V_{eff} is calculated to be: 4 x 40 = **160 litres**.

The larger volume of V_{eff} is calculated to be: 4 x 60 = **240 litres.**

If a cylinder that **combines solar and back-up heat** is to be used:

The smallest volume of V_{eff} is calculated to be: 4 x 40 = 160 litres. This is located below a standby volume (V_b) given to be 120 litres. A timer switching twice a day controls the standby volume hence from Table 4.3 the storage factor available to the solar is F = 0.3.

Hence the extra volume available to the solar = 0.3 x 120 = 36 litres.

Hence the dedicated solar storage V_s = 160 - 36 = 124 litres

Hence the overall size of the store (V_{total}) = V_s + V_b = 124 + 120

= **244 litres.**

The larger volume of V_{eff} is calculated to be: 4 x 60 = 240 litres.

Hence the extra volume available to the solar = 0.3 x 120 = 36 litres.

Hence the dedicated solar storage V_s = 240 - 36 = 204 litres

Hence the overall size of the store (V_{total}) = V_s + V_b = 204 + 120

= **324 litres.**

Once all the calculations are complete, it would be preferable to select the next commercially available size of store up from the calculated size. However, in the UK and Ireland, traditional airing cupboard sizes will be found to be too restrictive to accommodate the larger sizes of storage vessel. Where solar storage is undersized in relation to collector size, there will be decreasing ability to store peak summer gains from day to day and there will be a higher risk of over-heating components unless suitable precautions are taken. At larger collector areas, or where the occupants' DHW pattern is biased to daytime usage, the smaller range of storage values can be used. The range of solar storage should also be considered in relation to the expected performance of the collector. A lower efficiency collector of the same area is likely to provide less heat than one of high efficiency. A geographical location with low irradiance as taken from Figure 7.10 will also suggest the lower range of store size.

7.7.3   The effect of undersized solar storage

As is noted above, in the UK and Ireland it is often found that it is not possible to achieve the dedicated solar storage sizes suggested in Section 7.7.2. This leads to under-sizing with a consequence of reducing overall system performance particularly during summer.

At low storage volumes, the performance can be related to the daily DHW usage (V_d) independently of the collector size since, in effect, both the collector and solar storage are both highly dependent on the amount of energy used by the household for heating DHW. A calculation can be made to assess the performance reduction.

The first stage in the calculation requires the daily household DHW volume (V_d) at 55°C to be known, which is analysed in Section 7.5.4. From this it is possible to use the Figure 7.14 below to anticipate either the amount of annual energy that will be lost compared to the acceptable level or to ensure that an acceptable level is present. It can be seen that an acceptable performance requires the effective solar storage volume (V_{eff}) to exceed the daily household DHW volume (V_d).

> For the fullest collector performance, the effective solar storage volume should exceed the daily DHW draw-off :
>
> $$\mathbf{V_{eff} > V_d}$$

> **Worked example**
>
> The daily household DHW volume (V_d) at 55°C was found to be **120 litres.**
>
> The constraints of airing cupboard size and the requirement to store sufficient boiler heated water as standby mean that the twin coil cylinder has the following characteristics:
>
> Dedicated solar storage in the lower part of heat cylinder (V_s) = **50 litres**
>
> Standby boiler heated volume (V_b) = **95 litres**
>
> The storage factor (Table 7.8) available to the solar with a twice daily timer F = **0.3**
>
> Hence, the extra volume of standby volume available to the solar = 0.3 x 95 = **28.5 litres**
>
> Hence the effective solar storage V_{eff} = 28.5 + 50 litres = **78.5 litres**
>
> The storage ratio = V_{eff}/V_d = 78.5/120 = **0.65**
>
> From Figure 7.14, the annual solar energy will be **92%** of the potential collector performance .

Whilst it is clear from Figure 7.14 that under sizing the solar storage will reduce annual useful solar energy, it is also true that over sizing can do the same, albeit to a lesser extent. This is partly due to the larger surface area of the storage causing greater surface losses but also the increased frequency of additional non-solar heat sources being required to achieve the target DHW temperature. The higher limits shown in Table 7.9 allow for this although certain system types may use an even higher storage to collector ratio to reduce stagnation periods in summer.

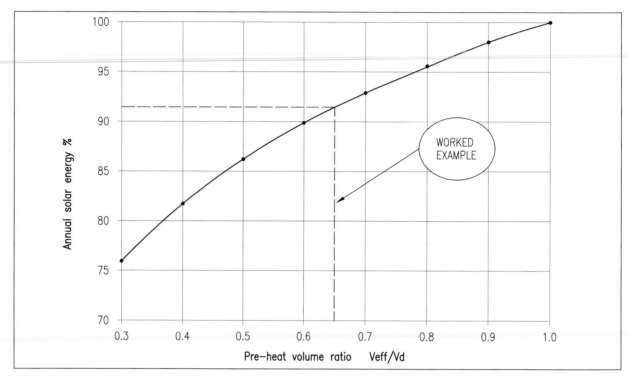

Figure 7.14 Loss of annual energy according to the storage volume ratio

7.8   Solar heat exchanger sizing

The primary circuit with the solar collector normally transfers heat to the secondary hot water via a heat exchanger. This heat exchanger is usually located within the dedicated solar storage volume but can be externally located as with plate heat exchangers. The heat exchanger should be designed to maintain a temperature in the return circuit to the collector as close as possible to the temperature of the incoming secondary cold feed to the store. To achieve this, the heat exchanger must be both large enough to transfer low-temperature heat and located as low as possible in the dedicated solar storage to benefit from stratification of the stored water.

In sizing the surface area of the heat exchanger, the following should be considered:

- Peak power reaching the heat exchanger is 500 Watts per m^2 of collector absorber.

- ΔT between the flow and return primary circuit is between 10 and 30 K.

- ΔT between the primary and secondary is between 5 and 10 K.

- Rate of circulation of primary fluid is 0.2 to 1.3 litres per minute per m^2 of collector absorber

In the case of internal heat exchangers, two types of coil design are frequently found, namely either plain round tube or finned tube. The latter has considerable extra surface area per running linear metre due to the fins, however it requires a larger comparative area due to the inefficiencies of heat transfer around the fins.

Hence, the following rules of thumb apply for internal heat exchangers for solar water heating:

- Finned tube   0.30 - 0.40 m² per m² collector absorber
- Plain tube   0.15 - 0.20 m² per m² collector absorber

Worked example

A collector is given an area of 4 m²

Calculate the options of coil area:

The coil smaller area option for finned tube	= 0.30 x 4 = 1.2 m²
The coil larger area option for finned tube	= 0.40 x 4 = 1.6 m²
The coil smaller area option for plain tube	= 0.15 x 4 = 0.6 m²
The coil larger area option for plain tube	= 0.20 x 4 = 0.8 m²

7.9   Pipe sizing and circulation rate

The diameter of pipe used in the primary circuit is varied according to the limiting dynamic pressure drop for a given circulation rate, but also with concerns for heat loss (Section 7.5.5) and volume content (Section 7.10) in relation to minimum pump run time. Circulation rates can be anticipated at the design stage but can also be accurately measured on site by the use of in-line circulation meters (see Section 6.1.4).

First consideration must be given to the chosen circulation rate through the collector, which then permits the velocity through the pipes to be calculated. At reduced rates, there can be problems of air-retention during commissioning, inadequate rate of heat removal under high irradiation conditions and poor balance of circulation distribution through the collector array. Too high a circulation rate reduces the temperature of the flow circuit, which in turn reduces stratification in the solar storage and can outstrip the capacity of the heat exchanger to absorb heat, hence artificially raising the return circuit temperature. This also increases noise. A circulation velocity in the pipes of between 0.3 - 0.7 metre per second is suggested. Above 1 metre per second can cause metal erosion.

There are two schools of thought in selecting the rate of collector circulation: namely low-rate or high-rate defined in Table 7.10.

Circulation through collector	Rate Litres per minute	Comments
High rate	0.5 to 1.2	Results in a higher dynamic pressure drop hence requires large pipe sizes. Ensures an even distribution across parallel collector array. Large volume content helps even out temperature swings, reduced temperature difference between flow/return and reduced boiling and antifreeze degradation.
Low rate	0.2 to 0.3	Allows smaller bore pipes to be used with less heat loss but only is possible with a series connection of collectors. Leads to higher temperatures and increased collector losses but provides better stratification in the store. There is a lower volume content hence less protection against steam reaching vulnerable system components. Requires good heat exchanger performance to compensate for increased collector losses.

Table 7.10 Characteristics of circulation rates levels

For large collector array of over 20 m², low-flow design brings large cost savings on pump and pipes. High efficiency performance collectors need particular care. For typical sizes of solar systems, it is possible to state basic rules-of-thumb related to collector area and to the pump speeds of standard domestic circulator pumps as shown below in Table 7.11.

Circulation rates 0.5 to 1.2 litres per minute							
Low Performance	High Performance	Total primary circuit circuit distance Metres					
Collector area m²	Collector area m²		10	20	30	40	50
Up to 3	Up to 5	Pipe diameter mm	15	15	15	15	15
3-10	5-10		15	22	22	22	22
10-15	10-15		22	22	22	28	28
20-25	20-25		22	28	28	28	35
25-30	20-25		35	35	35	35	42

Table 7.11 Pipe sizing according to collector area and circuit length

7.10   Volume content

A calculation of total system volume and collector volume is necessary to anticipate primary fluid quantities such as antifreeze but also to anticipate expansion of the fluid over all the expected temperature ranges. The system's volume is the summation of the volumes of the heat exchanger, pipes, expansion vessel and collector. The following Tables 7.12, 7.13 and 7.14 can assist in the calculation where manufacturer's data is missing. An allowance of 0.5 litres should be given for pumps, flow meter and associated components. For heat exchangers, allow 0.3 - 1.0 litres per m^2 of collector absorber. For expansion vessels, see Section 7.13.

	Copper to BS EN 1057 - R250 (Old Table X) - Outside diameter and wall thickness (mm)				
Pipe size	8 x 0.6	10 x 0.6	12 x 0.6	15 x 0.7	22 x 0.9
Volume litres per metre	0.036	0.058	0.085	0.145	0.321

Table 7.12 Volumetric quantities of copper tube diameters

	Threaded medium weight steel to BS 1387 - Nominal diameter				
Pipe size	3/8"	1/2"	3/4"	1"	11/4"
Volume litres per metre	0.12	0.2	0.37	0.58	1.02

Table 7.13 Volumetric quantities of steel tube diameters

Collector type	**Fluid content per m^2 of collector absorber**
Flat plate with pipes in absorber	0.6 - 1.2
Flat plate welded sheet absorber	1.0 - 1.6
Evacuated tube 'Sydney' flask	3.5 - 4.5
Evacuated tube full flow	1.5 - 2.5
Evacuated tubes heat-pipe	0.3 - 0 .6

Table 7.14 Volumetric quantities of collector types

7.11   Safety valve sizing

Where safety valves are used to protect against over-pressure in the collector arrays adjacent to the collector positions, they should be sized with an allowance for steam content. The following Table 7.15 below indicates approximate guidance for the nominal diameter of such valves. Where the main safety valve is located closer to the store, it can be sized for liquid only discharge and hence is slightly smaller than indicated. The valve is normally rated for pressure at the maximum intended design limit +10%, see also Section 4.13 for sizing expansion vessel. Typical valve ratings are 3, 5 or 6 bar, chosen to protect the weakest component in the system and to avoid unnecessary discharge to atmosphere, see also Section 6.2.2.

Collector absorber m²	Nominal valve diameter size DN mm
50	15
100	22
200	35

Table 7.15 Nominal safety valve sizes according to collector area

7.12   Pipework – mechanical properties

It should be noted that thermal linear expansion rates of materials such as copper pipe are far greater in solar circuits than in ordinary plumbing due to the extreme temperature differences. A minimum allowance of up to 3 mm expansion per linear metre should be allowed for most metal pipes between the coldest days and stagnation temperatures near the collector. The following Table 7.16 indicates that greater elongation may occur for softer copper types.

Copper pipe category	HARD (R290)	HALF HARD (R250)	ANNEALED (R220)
Elongation	> 3%	> 20%	> 40%

Table 7.16 Linear elongation of copper tube types

The temperature limitation of some common joints should be particularly noted especially where located adjacent to the collector and especially in the case of high performance evacuated tube collectors whose stagnation temperature can exceed 250°C. Table 7.17 indicates typical limitations of some common joint types although individual manufacturers may provide higher rated components. Specialist high temperature jointing materials for solar systems are recommended wherever possible.

Joint type	Pressure limit Bar	Operating temperature limit °C	Softening points of materials °C
Most non-metal bodied joints and non-metal pipes	6	95	110
Soft solder - lead based	16	110	140
Soft solder - lead free	16	110	160
Silver solder (hard solder)	16	110	200
Hard braze - Copper Phosphorus	16	110	850
Compression without support sleeves	6	120	N/A
O-ring with metal case low temperature	10	110	N/A
O-ring high with metal case high temperature	16	200	N/A

Table 7.17 Characteristics of common joints

For example, the use of flat face unions with fibre faced washers, compression olives with support sleeves and threaded joints using hemp have proven performance in solar systems at high temperatures and pressures. Flux of any kind should be avoided where possible and flushed out if used. There is increasing use of high temperature o-rings with copper crimp fittings as a reliable jointing technique. Pipework for solar circuits not only has to withstand high temperatures but also mechanical damage from sharp edges whilst passing though the roof covering. Rodent attack is highly likely, either above the roof from birds and squirrels or at ceiling level in the loft from mice or rats. Non-metallic pipes are not recommended in these situations.

Pipe insulation should be selected for its high temperature resistance, above 150°C, even several metres away from the collectors. In general only two types are commonly used; either foil-faced mineral wool or flexible nitrile rubber. Both are susceptible to rodent attack, particularly externally, hence, extra mechanical protection such as metal cladding or petroleum wrap should be used.

Pipe fixings should be metallic where in contact with metallic pipes in the solar circuits. For reduced heat-loss, pipe fixings that clamp over the pipe insulation can be used.

Both sensor and power cables should be protected from sharp edges and rodent attack, externally or where passing through ceilings or roof coverings. One way to readily achieve this is to use special flexible pre-insulated pipes specifically made for solar installations. These incorporate high temperature cables within continuous insulation covering convoluted single-wall stainless steel or copper pipe. Further mechanical protection may still be required against rodents.

7.13   Dimensioning of membrane expansion vessels

In a fully-filled, sealed primary system a membrane expansion vessel is a vital component which is required in order to enable the installation to achieve "hydraulic security" in harmony with BS EN 12976. This is further discussed in Section 5.5. The over-pressure safety valve should not be triggered, even when the highest possible operating pressure is reached, usually during stagnation. Furthermore, the expansion vessel size and its adjustable gas pressure also affects the selection of the boil point of the antifreeze. The boil point temperature should be carefully selected as if it is too high it can result in the premature degradation of the antifreeze. Under sizing of the expansion vessels and over-pressurising of the system, therefore, can raise the boil point of the anti-freeze.

The size of the expansion vessel is related to the volume of fluid liable to expand, see Section 2.4, as well as the difference in height between the vessel and the top of the collector. The vessel gas-side and system side pressures can be adjusted to achieve the rquired performance. Table 7.18 below indicates suggested sizes for the expansion vessel and associated pressure settings in order to avoid unnecessary safety valve discharge. A more detailed calculation follows in Appendix D and this should be used where there is doubt. The nearest next largest commercial sizes of expansion vessels are shown in Tables 7.18 and 7.19. As can be seen, the vessel sizes are much larger than are used for a typical central heating system and it can be an advantage to operate using 6 Bar safety valves, as they allow smaller vessel sizes and hence require less antifreeze. However, undersized vessels will lead to greater pressure fluctuations between hot and cold. Where it is decided to increase the durability of the antifreeze by decreasing the point of vaporisation, the vessel nominal size should be increased even further. If in doubt, the larger size should always be used.

In particularly cold regions, the gas side pre-charge can be dropped marginally lower to provide extra volume of fluid to cover the contraction of the fluid. For systems that have poor emptying characteristics, see Section 7.17, greater steam generation is more likely when approaching stagnation and the next largest vessel size should be considered along with greater protection to the vessel membrane.

For detailed expansion vessel calculations and examples, see Appendix D. Some manufacturers can provide commercial software calculations which greatly simply this method.

System height Metres	2.5	5	10
System volume Litres	**VESSEL SIZE/GAS SIDE PRE-CHARGE/INITIAL FILL** Litres / Bar / Bar		
<10	25 / 0.8 / 1.1	25 / 1.0 / 1.3	50 / 1.5 / 1.8
20	35 / 0.8 / 1.1	50 / 1.0 / 1.3	75 / 1.5 / 1.8
30	50 / 0.8 / 1.1	60 / 1.0 / 1.3	100 / 1.5 / 1.8
40	60 / 0.8 / 1.1	75 / 1.0 / 1.3	120 / 1.5 / 1.8
50	75 / 0.8 / 1.1	100 / 1.0 / 1.3	150 / 1.5 / 1.8

Table 7.18 Nominal expansion vessel settings with a 3 bar safety valve and 0.5 bar overpressure

Although using a high safety over-pressure value does permit a smaller vessel whilst retaining hydraulic security, consideration to using the larger vessel sizes will assist in increasing the durability of antifreeze by lowering system pressure when hot and hence reducing the vaporisation point.

System height Metres	2.5	5	10
System volume Litres	**VESSEL SIZE/GAS SIDE PRE-CHARGE/INITIAL FILL** Litres / Bar / Bar		
<10	18 / 1.3 / 1.6	18 / 1.5 / 1.8	18 / 2.0 / 2.3
20	25 / 1.3 / 1.6	25 / 1.5 / 1.8	35 / 2.0 / 2.3
30	35 / 1.3 / 1.6	35 / 1.5 / 1.8	40 / 2.0 / 2.3
40	40 / 1.3 / 1.6	50 / 1.5 / 1.8	50 / 2.0 / 2.3
50	50 / 1.3 / 1.6	50 / 1.5 / 1.8	60 / 2.0 / 2.3

Table 7.19 Nominal expansion vessel settings with a 6 bar safety valve and 1.0 bar overpressure

7.14   Dimensioning of drainback vessels

The sizing of drainback vessels is simpler than for fully filled membrane vessels since:

- Measures to prevent steam reaching the membrane are not required

- Extra vapour volume upon stagnation is not calculated

However, they do require calculation of:

- Air pocket volume

- Tidal (quiescent) volume

A safety over-pressure valve is also required in a sealed system, typically at 3 Bar. Table 7.20 below indicates suggested sizes for drainback vessels. A more detailed calculation follows in the next section and if in doubt should be used.

For detailed drainback vessel calculations and examples, see Appendix E.

In general, the pressure in a drainback system with adequately sized volumes will oscillate between zero and 1.5 Bar, between hot and cold. The pressure may even fall below the boiling point of the fluid at temperatures approaching 100°C in the collector during drainback. In particular, for tall systems, care is required to choose the correct pump to reach the static height of the collector and to attend to the risk of low temperature boiling and noise.

Collector size m²	2.8	4.2	5.5	8.2
	Drainback sizes - Litres			
Liquid volume of system	15	16	17	26
Air volume of system	3.5	4.5	5.5	8
Total volume of system	18.5	20.5	22.5	34
Tidal volume	2.7	3.5	4.5	6.5
Air pocket in expansion vessel	0.8	0.8	0.8	1.3
Total nominal vessel size	10	10	20	19

Table 7.20 Dimensioning of drainback vessels

7.15   Pump sizing and dynamic pressure drop

Reference to the relevant circulator and worksheet section of the Domestic Heating Guide Appendix A7 should be made in relation to this section.

Once a circulation rate through the collector is selected, see Section 7.9, along with the primary pipe and heat exchanger sizes, it is possible to calculate the overall dynamic pressure drop and hence the minimum pump size. It is worth noting that a drainback system requires special consideration, as for part of the pumping cycle it is acting as if on an open-ended circuit until a siphon forms over the top of the collector. In this respect, the pump must be oversized when compared to a fully filled system pump and be required to reach the static head between the top of the collector and the vessel. See also Section 6.2.5.

For typical sizes of household solar DHW systems, the circulation rates indicated in Section 7.9 are well below those found in central heating systems, which have much higher peak power. For this reason, the dynamic pressure drop is usually found to be quite minimal and most conventional tables of data do not provide great detail at such low rates. For larger solar systems, an estimate of the total system pumping characteristic can be derived by using Figures 7.15 to 7.17 to identify the dynamic pressure drop for the collector, pipes and heat exchangers. For smaller systems, Table 7.21 provides some default figures. Where using other references for dynamic pressure drop, it should be noted that, when compared to water, antifreeze causes approximately 1.3 times the resistance. Glycol water mixed antifreeze can also become significantly more resistive near to its freezing point.

Item	Pressure drop mbar at 3 litres/minute
Flat plate collector	150
Heat-pipe collector	30
Coil heat exchanger	5
Plate exchanger	5
Flow and return copper pipes @ 10 mm diameter	12.0 / metre. If total circuit is 10 m total pipe pressure drop is 120
Flow and return copper pipes @ 15 mm diameter	4.5 / metre. If total circuit is 10 m total pipe pressure drop is 45
Flow and return copper pipes @ 22 mm diameter	1.0 / metre. If total circuit is 10 m total pipe pressure drop is 10
Pipe fittings including check valves	30% of total pipe pressure drop
Total system pressure drop	**Sum of Pressure drops of Collector + Exchanger + Pipe fittings**

Table 7.21 Default values for dynamic pressure drop of a glycol water mix circulating in a typical small solar DHW primary system

It should be noted that:

- For collectors or exchangers in series, the individual pressure drop losses are summed

- For similar collectors or exchangers in parallel, the total is equal to that of one item

- If otherwise unknown, for pipe fittings add 30% losses to the value found for the pipes

Figure 7.18 shows a typical characteristic against a typical domestic circulating pump. The ideal pump would be chosen so that the working point is in the middle of the pump characteristic line as this represents the best efficiency. However there are not many pumps on the market that meet this desirable criterion in full, hence a compromise is usually required. At this point it may be worth considering if the electrical energy used to drive the pump could be reduced either by choosing a different circulation rate, different collector layout, a high efficiency pump (according to the Europump A-G scale) or a variable speed pump, see also Section 6.1.3.

A system characteristic can be plotted against a range of pump characteristics to identify intersections and hence identify potential operating points.

Manufacturers supply the pump characteristics whereas the system characteristic is derived from a single circulation rate such as from Tables 7.10 and 7.21 above.

Since a proportional increase in the circulation rate will cause the same proportional increase in dynamic pressure, it is then possible to plot further pressure drops against various circulation rates. A system curve can then be drawn. The following equation indicates the relationship between scenario (a) and scenario (b) :

$$\frac{\text{Rate}^2\ a}{\text{Rate}^2\ b} = \frac{\text{Pressure}_{dynamic}\ a}{\text{Pressure}_{dynamic}\ b}$$

Worked example

The dynamic pressure drop is known to be 185 mbar at 3 litres per minute. At 10 litres per minute, the drop = 185 x (10 x 10) / (3 x 3)

= 2056 mbar

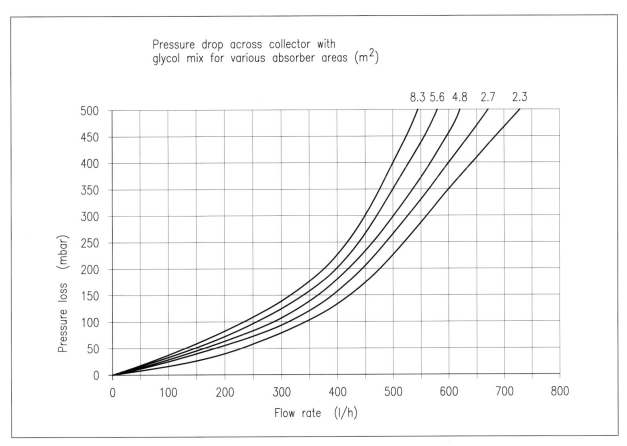

Figure 7.15 Dynamic pressure loss of aqueous glycol in flat plate collectors

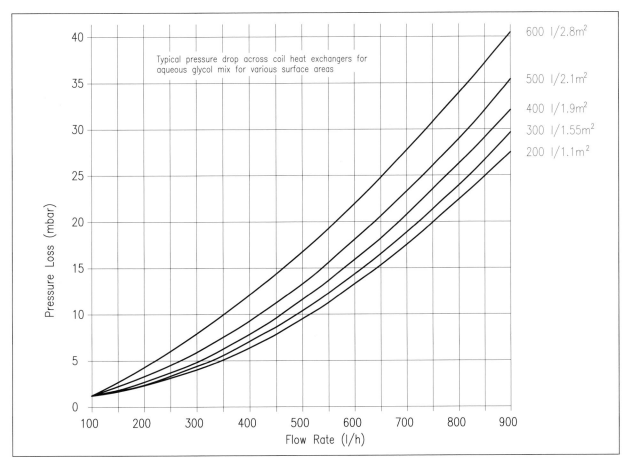

Figure 7.16 Dynamic pressure loss of aqueous glycol coil exchangers

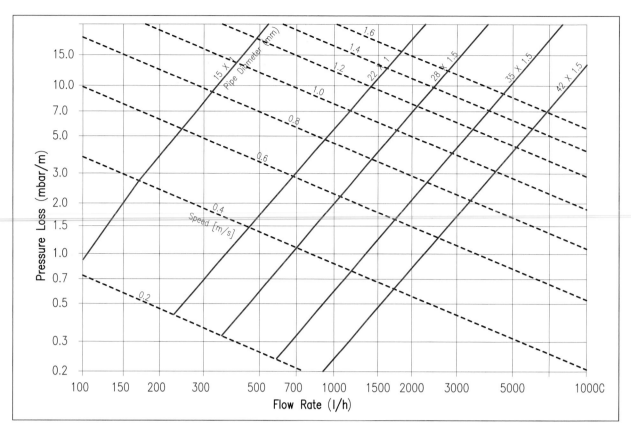

Figure 7.17 Dynamic pressure loss of aqueous glycol in pipes

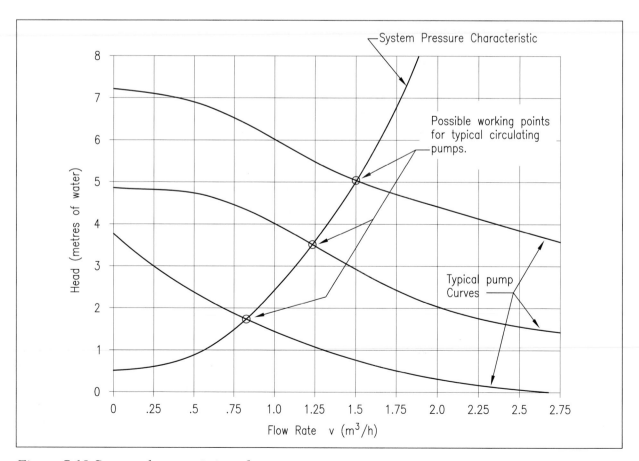

Figure 7.18 System characteristics of pumps

The specific heat capacity of antifreeze is lower than that of water, over all normal operating temperatures as shown in Figure 7.19. This implies that to transfer energy at the same rate, the antifreeze must be moved more quickly than plain water. If the rate of circulation remains the same, the temperature of the antifreeze will be higher than that of water, potentially causing inefficiency in the collector. Antifreeze is also more viscous than water and in general, a pump will have to work harder and use more electrical power with antifreeze than with plain water.

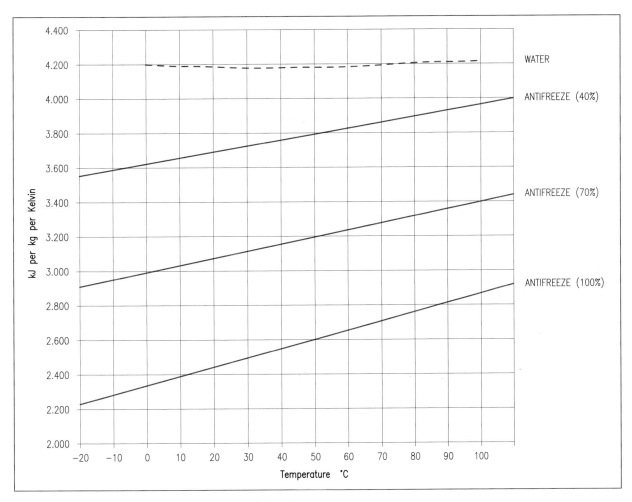

Figure 7.19 Specific heat capacities of fluids

7.16 Attributes of primary fluids

7.16.1 Boiling temperature with glycol concentrations

The choice of the boil point in a fully filled, sealed system is critical to the long-term durability of the antifreeze. The boil point can be adjusted by the choice of the initial filling pressure, expansion vessel nominal volume and the gas-side pressure of the vessel. Temperatures in the liquid phase below 130°C are considered preferable and the pump controller should be adjusted to cease circulation at this point to avoid cool liquid re-entering the extremely hot absorber. Upon vaporisation, only a few molecules of gaseous antifreeze will remain in the absorber, which is incidental to the overall quantity of liquid in the system. The technique of designing a system with a large enough solar storage but also permitting easy vaporisation from the collector, is the key requirement to achieve long term durability of fully-filled systems. See also Section 5.5, Section 7.13 and Figure 7.20.

Some collectors, such as evacuated tubes with integral heat pipes, can avoid vaporisation under any irradiation conditions if they are maintained at greater than 4 Bar in harmony with their self-limiting temperature response. However, prolonged exposure to high temperatures will cause degradation of the polypropylene glycol, causing permanent fractional distillation, formation of sludge and increase of acidity that can eventually corrode components such as steel and rubber membranes as well as block passageways and decrease the efficiency of absorbers.

7.16.2   Boiling points of plain water

Where plain water is used, such as in sealed system drainback collectors, the system pressure can range from below atmospheric to well above, depending on the initial fill setting and the ratio of air and liquid in the system. This affects the boiling point of the water. The air that is present will act partly as a cushion to absorb expansion and so reduce the potential rise in pressure. The pressure in each of part of the system is affected not only by the static height but also by the dynamic pressure of the pump. In a drain back system, boiling is most likely to occur in the collector just after the pump is switched off and the water is starting to drain away. The boiling point of plain water will vary according to the pressure as shown in Figure 7.21. Boiling can have undesirable effects of excess noise and reverberations in pipework.

7.16.3   Freezing point of glycol concentration

The concentration of glycol should be chosen depending on the lowest expected ambient temperature. It should be noted that the collector could become cooler than ambient temperature on a cloudless night due to the 'black-body' effect emitting radiation. Hence, a generous over-protection should be provided which also allows for the ageing process of glycol. Glycol decays under the action of heat, oxygen and bacteria hence regular checks on its acidity and concentration should be made. See Figure 7.22.

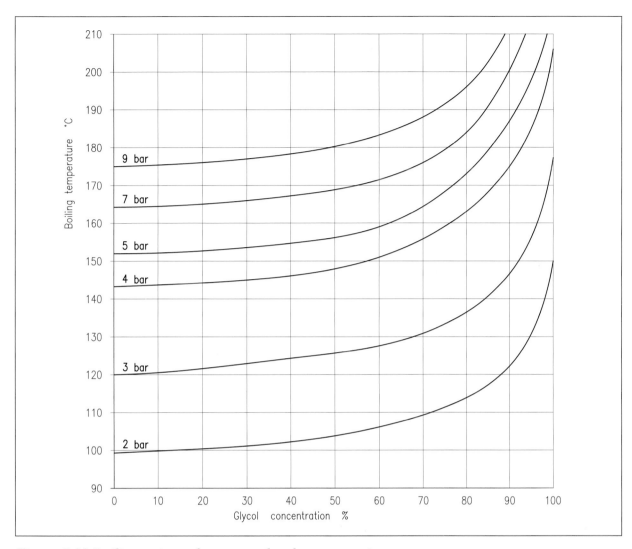

Figure 7.20 Boiling points of aqueous glycol concentrations

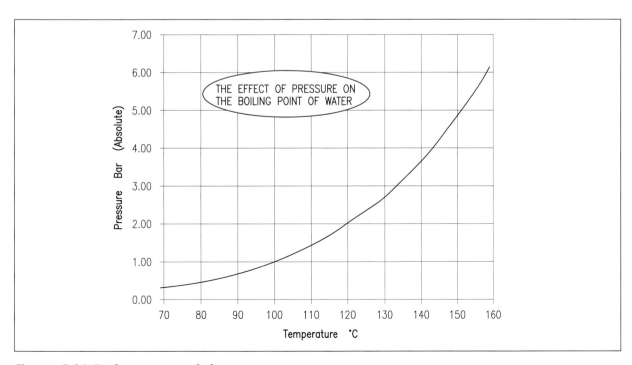

Figure 7.21 Boiling points of plain water

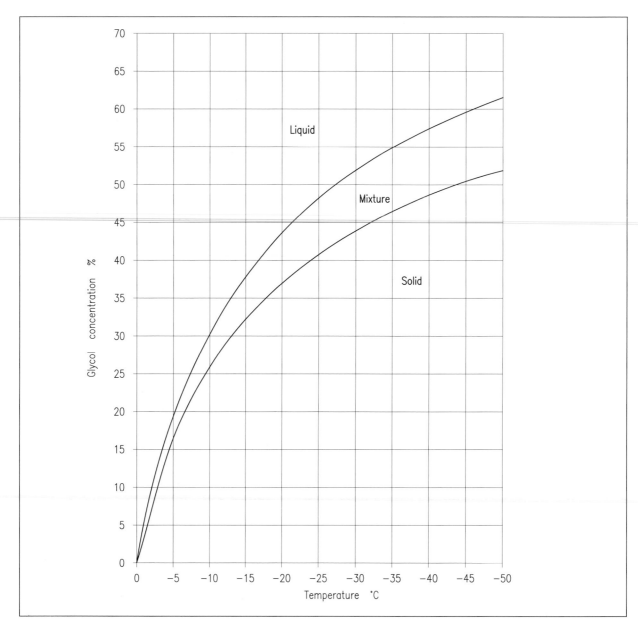

Figure 7.22 Freezing points of aqueous glycol concentrations

7.17   Arrangement of solar collector circuits

To reduce transport and lifting problems, many collectors are supplied in small units, nominally from 1 to 5m² area. Hence, larger areas are built up from these smaller units and this requires careful design of the plumbing inter-connections to ensure adequate balancing of circulation between each collector.

The simplest inter-connection layout is the series or in-line sequence as shown below in Figure 7.23. There are variants shown dependant on whether there are two or four pipe connections on each collector and whether the connections are at the same height or diagonally opposite. Whilst series connections are simple and use the least interconnecting pipe, they also create an increasing temperature gradient across the array that is a more significant disadvantage with low circulation rates and low efficiency collectors. Furthermore, the dynamic pressure resistance increases with each additional collector, ultimately limiting the number of collectors that can be connected this way. The choice of pumps becomes difficult in such designs. System designs using drainback or thermo-siphoning generally cannot use series connection. Dependant on the internal construction of the absorber, some collectors lend themselves to series connection better than others by containing internal manifolds and distribution channels. Before designing such arrangements a clear statement by the collector manufacturer of the dynamic pressure resistance measured to BS EN 12975 and the series connection limit should be sought. Care should also be taken to allow for linear pipe expansion within the array.

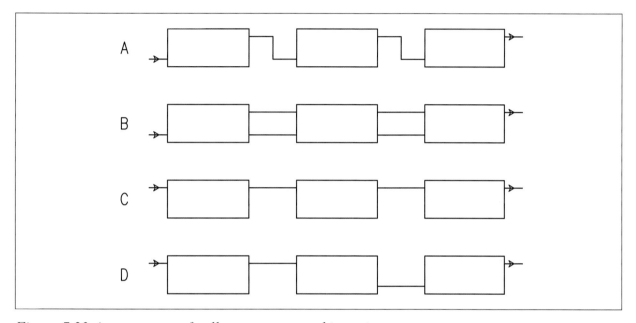

Figure 7.23 Arrangement of collectors connected in series

In the examples in Figure 7.23, care should also be given as to how the fluid will behave when approaching stagnation where a fully filled system is used. In this situation, where the pump is assumed to have stopped under high irradiation, the fluid will often be pushed out of the collector as it approaches the vaporisation point. This point is mainly determined by the system pressure and antifreeze concentration. The vaporising fluid will attempt to push out any remaining fluid towards the expansion vessel, normally on the return pipe i.e. against the normal circulation flow. However, in sequences A, C and D, this causes the vaporising antifreeze in the right-hand side collector of the series to pass through the high point of the left-hand collector where it is hottest. This situation can be compared to sequence B, where the fluid is most easily pushed through the lower pipe connection hence quickly into a cooler portion of the collector series.

In arrangements with poor emptying characteristics, steam locks can easily form, trapping un-evaporated liquid in the collector and placing this liquid under great stress from increasing temperatures. Eventually this liquid forms super-heated steam that can then pass out of the collector and have powerful effects far away from the collector. This effect can be measured as steam power. Good emptying characteristics will limit this power to 50 W/m² of absorber area, however poor characteristics will lead to over 120 W/m². Considering that even an insulated pipe at steam generation temperatures only loses heat at a rate approaching 25 W/m, it can be seen that with poor design there is a high likelihood of steam travelling down the circuit pipes to the storage area.

The behaviour of fluid in collectors during vaporisation is affected by the design of the waterways both in the collector and by the connecting system pipes. For flat plates, the return pipe will ideally always fall away downwards from the collector to assist the forming vapour to push-out fluid contents without forming steam locks. The positioning of the expansion vessel on the return line sets the direction of fluid expansion during stagnation, down the return, whereas the vapour does not normally expand through the flow pipes due to check valves located near the cylinder.

Evacuated tube collectors can be purchased with heat pipe configurations that contain self-limiting bi-metallic springs, which reduce heat transfer at temperatures above pre-determined limits such as 95°C or 130°C. This can reduce wear and tear on the antifreeze. Another configuration for tubes is to locate a manifold at the bottom or side of the tubes to encourage good vaporisation behaviour into the return line.

The alternative to a series connection is parallel connection as indicated below in Figure 7.24. This reduces the overall dynamic pressure resistance and maintains a similar temperature gradient across each collector and tends to equalise the pressure drops across the collectors.

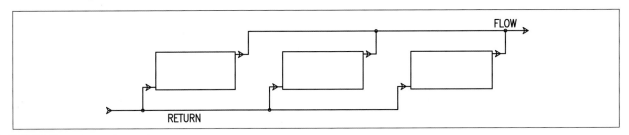

Figure 7.24 Arrangement of collectors connected in parallel

Note that to avoid any short-circuit and improve balancing, a reverse return arrangement below in Figure 7.25 is used where both pipes approach from the same direction.

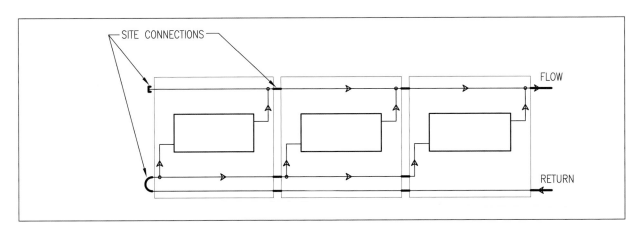

Figure 7.25 Arrangement of collectors connected in parallel piped from the same side

To ensure optimum uniform circulation is maintained though each collector, the Tichelmann principle is required which requires that the ratio of dynamic resistance of each collector be at least three times more than that of the pipes. A combination of series and parallel connections can be built up to create a large collector area with low overall dynamic pressure in which case each series sub-array is also kept over the 3:1 ratio. In some cases, the Tichelmann parallel principle is designed into the absorber pipes inside the collector so that multiple collectors can be series-connected, creating a long parallel manifold. An example of pipe sizing being used to create the Tichelmann principle is shown in Figure 7.26, where the interconnecting pipes between the collectors are 22mm diameter copper and the branch connections through each collector are 10mm diameter copper.

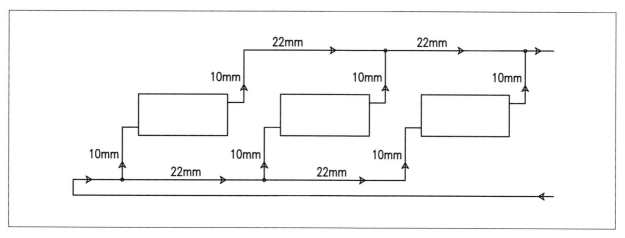

Figure 7.26 Schematic example of the Tichelmann principle of piping

When considering the behaviour of the fluid under stagnation in a fully filled system, it will be seen that providing the return pipe is kept lower than the collectors, the vaporising fluid will be easily able to push out remaining fluid towards the expansion vessel on the return in a parallel arrangement. Some collector manufacturers include an integral return manifold pipe within the casing of the collector enabling a much simpler external piping arrangement from one end of the array.

8.   Installation

8.1   Technical site survey

The procedure for technical site surveys will be different when comparing existing dwellings to those yet to be built (new-build). In either case, however, a standard checklist can be used to ensure that the important factors are taken into account. With new-build, the survey in effect takes place from drawings, whereas existing dwellings should be personally visited. The list below gives an indication of the main points to consider:

- Shading

- Collector fixing surface, pitch and orientation

- Collector fixing area, structure and covering

- Access to collector location

- Back-up DHW heat sources

- Pre-heat storage locations

- Secondary water pressure

- Water quality

- Occupant's DHW usage pattern

8.2   Selecting specialist tools

- Access – working at height regulations frequently require the use of specialised access equipment, including eaves-level platforms, steel scaffold or towers, cranes or hoists.

- Commissioning pump – these are special high flow rate pumps designed to rapidly fill solar primary systems and remove air or steam locks.

- Hand pumps – these are used for injecting extra antifreeze initially or during maintenance.

- Refractrometers – for sampling antifreeze concentrations. Alternatively, hydrometers can be used.

- PH testers – these are usually coloured impregnated strips that can identify loss of corrosion protection. i.e. degree of acidity or alkalinity.

- Hand-held pressure gauge – used for setting expansion vessel, accurate to BS EN 837-1. This should be regularly calibrated by a specialist supplier.

- High temperature brazing – this is used where soft solder joints are unsuitable at stagnation temperatures.

- Crimping tools – used with special high temperature o-ring fittings.

- Covers – these are to stop irradiation reaching the absorber during installation.

8.3   Initial testing

During the initial testing of a solar primary system, there is a high risk of scalding from stagnation heat built up in the absorber. When first filled, there can be an immediate steam flash and an intense heat shock to components. During prolonged periods with no heat extraction, unwanted oxides can form on internal collector surfaces reducing heat transfer. Collectors should therefore remain covered until initial testing has been completed. Unexpected leaks and emergency drain downs are best dealt with when the transfer fluid is cold.

It is inevitable that unwanted particles and chemicals will get into components during pipe laying, so a primary system should first be flushed cold, then hot until clear. However, great care must be taken to ensure that residual water is not unintentionally left in the system to dilute the antifreeze. Furthermore, if the system is left out of use for long periods without antifreeze in winter conditions, pockets of water could freeze or corrode components such as pump rotors.

Once the system is shown to be leak-free and operational, a prolonged pressure test is recommended. Air is not a suitable test medium due to the danger of gaseous explosions and the inability to discern temperature fluctuations. In systems where antifreeze is to be used, its use in the initial pressure test is to be preferred due its 'searching' qualities.

Solar pre-heat stores made from copper need to form an oxide layer on the interior surface to reduce corrosion risks. They should not, therefore, be left for long periods filled with unheated cold water. Briefly heating the store beyond 60°C will permit this oxide layer to form. Sacrificial or electrical anodes can also assist with reducing corrosion.

Except for pre-tested and continuous unbroken pipework runs used without joints or fittings, pipes should only be insulated after final pressure testing. Guidance for pressure testing is given in BS EN 14336.

Placing the pump control temperature sensors into a hot water bath before installation will allow a check to be made of their accuracy. Checking temperatures using an accurate digital readout temperature sensor will allow inaccurate sensors to be discarded. Collector temperature sensors can be susceptible to the absorption of unwanted moisture from prolonged temperature differentials and humidity. Special heat paste applied into sensor pockets reduces the possibility of this occurring.

8.4   Structural considerations

8.4.1   Wind and snow loads

Solar collectors impart two kinds of loads onto their mounting surface:

● Static (dead weight)

● Imposed (snow, wind)

The imposed loads are particularly variable due to weather conditions and can be affected by the exact position and shape of the collector. Imposed loads can occasionally be negative (lifting) and can be complex when they arise from the interaction of airflow around nearby obstacles. A structural engineer would normally be responsible for calculating such loads, however the following tables are indicative of some of the potential worst case values for flat plate collectors on roof pitches between 20° and 45°. Figure 8.1 below indicates the components of the loads relevant to the analysis of such forces. All forces are expressed in Newtons noting that a kilogram has a force from gravity of approximately 10 Newtons at sea level. Forces may be combined, such as with snow and wind or snow along with the dead weight hence these components should be added together for the total force affecting the collector. Where doubt exists, further guidance is available from BS 6399, BS EN 1991 and BRE Digest 489 (Wind based loads on roof-based photovoltaic systems).

It is also recommended that the roof covering, either adjacent to a roof integrated collector or beneath an above roof mounted collector, is mechanically fixed to adequately resist the wind uplift load calculated in accordance with BS 6399 and BS 5534.

All tiles near solar collectors should be mechanically fixed in place. It is particularly important for above roof mounted collectors that the roof covering beneath them should be mechanically fixed to the requirements for local roof areas as defined in BS 5534. This is because of the potential for acceleration of wind speed beneath the collector creating high levels of suction.

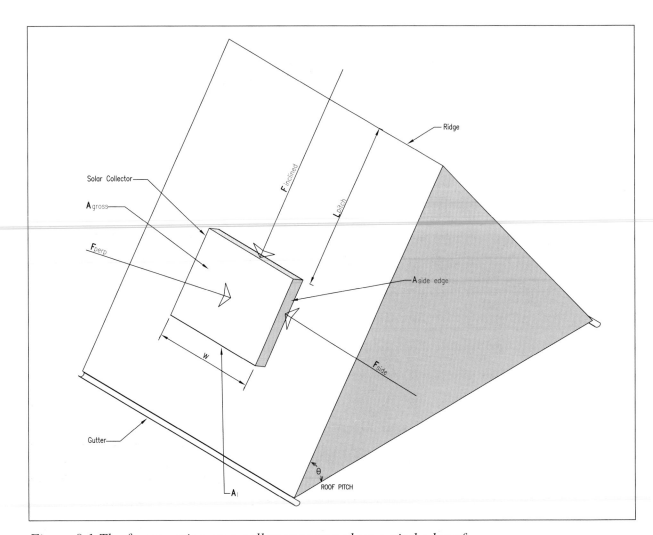

Figure 8.1 The forces acting on a collector mounted on a pitched roof

M	kg	Mass of collector with fluid
A_l	m²	Area of low edge
A_{gross}	m²	Overall area of front of collector
$A_{sideedge}$	m²	Area of collector side
F_{perp}	N	Force applied perpendicular to collector
$F_{inclined}$	N	Force down on collector edge
F_{side}	N	Force applied to collector side
W	m	Width collector across the pitch
L_{pitch}	m	Distance from top of the collector to the ridge line

Table 8.1 The forces acting on a collector mounted on a pitched roof

Potential dead loads where M = Mass of collector		
$Force_{perp}$ N	$Force_{inclined}$ N	$Force_{side}$ N
0.94 x M x 9.81	0.71 x M x 9.81	0

Table 8.2 Table of static loads on collector

Potential snow load up to 200m altitude in England. Collector held clear of typical pitched roof			
$Force_{perp}$ N	$Force_{inclined}$ N	$Force_{inclined}$ N	$Force_{side}$ N
	Lying snow	Sliding snow If collector projects above roof	
864 x A_{gross}	500 x A_{gross}	500 x W x L_{pitch}	0

Table 8.3 Table of snow loads on collector

Potential wind loads at 48 metres per second					
	$Force_{perp}$ N			$Force_{inclined}$ N	$Force_{side}$ N
	Maximum outward		Maximum inward		
	Distributed	Localised at leading edge	Distributed	Distributed	Distributed
No protrusion above plane of roof	- 1692 x A gross	0	+ 1410 x A gross	0	0
Up to 150 mm. protrusion above roof	- 2115 x A gross	- 5076 x A sideedge	+ 1410 x A gross	± 2256 x A lowedge	± 2256 x A sideedge
Up to 150mm gap between bottom of collector and plane of roof	- 705 x A gross	- 5076 x A sideedge	+ 1551 x A gross	± 4230 x A lowedge	± 4230 x A sideedge
Notes		Either edge: $A_{sideedge}$ or $A_{lowedge}$			

Table 8.4 Table of wind loads on collector

Potential loads on a free standing collector		
		Notes
Dead weight N	W	Vertically
Snow load N	$\pm$ 0.3 x 960 x A$_{gross}$	Vertically
Wind load N	$\pm$ 0.3 x 960 x A$_{gross}$	Perpendicular to collector
	$\pm$ 0.3 x 960 x A$_{sideedge}$	Either edge: A$_{sideedge}$ or A$_{lowedge}$

Table 8.5 Table of loads on a free standing collector

Example total load combination Newtons for a 1.5 m² flat plate collector held clear of roof fixings					
Force$_{perp}$ N			Force$_{inclined}$ N		Force$_{side}$ N
Inward	Outward	Sides	Down roof plane	Up roof plane	Across roof place
2742	- 643	- 1167 & - 761	2560	- 322	$\pm$ 973

Table 8.6 Example loads on a collector mounted on a pitched roof

8.4.2   Fixing

The method of fixing solar collectors to roofs varies considerably for different roof types and collector designs. The following guidance is not designed to replace manufacturer's fixing instructions in new systems but may be useful where a collector of unknown origin is to be fitted or replaced. No guidance is offered here regarding collectors that are integrated into the roof covering or vertically mounted collectors, as these require specialist structural advice.

Collectors mounted above the roof covering are commonplace in the UK and Ireland. To achieve this a bracket must hold the collector to the roof structure and the roof is therefore altered from its original design loading. This has structural and durability implications and due care is required. For installations intended to meet the Roofing Industry Alliance Hallmark Scheme, minimum competence levels for this work are recognised including Construction Skills certificate scheme 'A' (CITB NVQ 2) for typical pitched roofs.

Aside from this, relevant standards and codes for roofing are shown in Table 8.7:

General and pitched roofs	BS 8000, BS 6399, BS 5534, NFRC, BS EN 1991 Part 2
Flat supported (Felt, asphalt, liquid)	BS 6229, BS 8217, BS 8218, FRCAB, NFRC, ELRA
Flat self-supporting (metal profile, fibre-cement)	BS 5427, CP143, MCRMA, NFRC
Metal supported (copper, zinc, lead, aluminium)	BS 6915, CP143, LSA, MCRMA

Table 8.7 Table of roofing guidance

British Standard Code of Practice	Metal Cladding and Roofing Manufacturers Association Limited
Construction Industry Training Board	National Federation Roofing Contractor
European Liquid Roofing Association	National Vocational Qualification
Flat Roofing Contractors Advisory Board	Roofing Industry Alliance
Lead Sheet Association	Metal Cladding and Roofing Manufacturers Association Limited

Table 8.8 Table of roof industry organisations and categories

8.4.3 Temperature of pipes

Stagnation temperatures (where there is no heat extraction under full sunshine) can lead to internal solar collector fluid temperatures in excess of 150°C, dependant on the collector type. This temperature can conduct through pipe walls and collector edges. Adjoining components such as pipes supports, pipe insulation and electrical connections must be designed to withstand this temperature.

Pipes, pipe insulation and pipe supports in particular should be selected on the basis of suitability for containing super-heated steam. Metallic pipes and supports have a proven capability in this respect. Foil-faced mineral wool and high temperature nitrile rubber pipe insulation also have a long-standing history in this application.

8.4.4   Weatherproofing

All external components must be designed to take account of ultra-violet and ozone degradation, storm force winds, salt spray, snow loads and rodent attack. They should also be resistant to any additives to the heat transfer fluid that may be spilt such as anti-freeze and any sharp edges present when passing through the roof. Pipe insulation, where external, should be of the high temperature and of the non-absorbent (closed-cell) type.

As a rule, the layout should be planned to minimize external pipe runs, even if simply to reduce heat loss. External pipe fixings are difficult to secure across both pitched and flat roofs, but where used should be corrosion resistant. On pitched roofs, these can be formed from metal strips located under tiles. On flat roofs, ballast weights may be useful. In all cases, water drainage must be considered and, ideally, the pipe raised to allow debris and snow to clear. Low voltage sensor or power cables requiring support are usually clipped to the insulation over the pipe, unless built as suggested in Section 7.12.

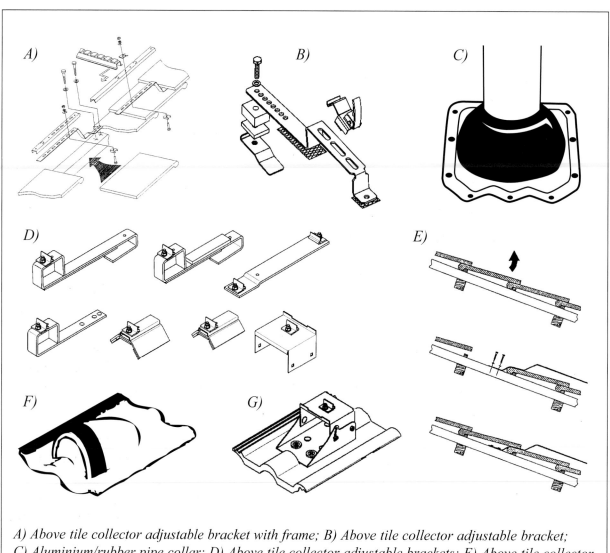

A) Above tile collector adjustable bracket with frame; B) Above tile collector adjustable bracket;
C) Aluminium/rubber pipe collar; D) Above tile collector adjustable brackets; E) Above tile collector adjustable bracket; F) Ventilation tile; G) Plastic tile with moulded collector bracket

Figure 8.2

The solar trade in the UK and Ireland has historically used silicone sealant around pipes and cables penetrating roofs. Where this continues, the sealant should retain at least 50% flexibility and be resistant to ultra-violet degradation. Where in contact with the pipes, the sealant should also be resistant to temperatures up to 150°C. Reference to such sealants can be made using ISO 11600, BS 6213 or BS 5889. Furthermore, the sealant should only be applied in dry conditions, with ambient air temperatures above 5°C. Fixing should only be onto a suitably prepared clean surface and the sealant should be tooled to ensure adhesion.

Good practice requires use of proprietary or custom metal flashing. There may also be options using propriety soil vent products, however these do not normally allow continuous insulation though the penetration. A solution that may allow this would be a deep-dish 'eyebrow' ventilator tile (approx. 30cm² free air) commonly used by the solar industry in Europe. Underlay penetration is unavoidable with pipes and cables connecting solar collectors through pitched roofs. Where air tightness and insulation levels are to be retained, proprietary eyebrow tiles with purpose designed aprons and ducts may be the only viable solution. For certain roof types, proprietary flashings may not be available requiring the use of flexible sealants and custom flashings.

It is worth noting that existing UK roofing guidance makes little or no reference to solar collectors as yet, however the following is regarded as general good practice in respect of pitched tiles or slates:

- Maintain access to the roof covering beneath the collector.

- Impart no loads (static, wind or snow) onto the roof covering.

- Design the loads onto substantial roof structures i.e. rafters, purlins, trusses.

- Provide sufficient lap of flashing where tiles are cut or raised.

- Allow for negative pressure lifting adjoining components.

For pitched tiles or slates, existing practice in the solar trade since the 1970's has tended towards the use of malleable aluminium or stainless steel straps laid under tiles and screwed onto rafter tops. Aluminium angle extrusions can be screwed onto rafters through drilled holes in tiles. It should be noted these techniques may impart loads onto the roof tiles. For modern, single lap interlocking tiles, there is increased use of pre-formed, rigid stainless steel brackets fixed to rafters under the tiles. Pre-manufactured plastic tiles with integral steel mounts that replace whole tiles are also used, although these require a minimum batten size. Screwed fixings tend to be stainless steel.

Both slates and solid stone slabs are common in UK and Ireland and difficulties due to their non-accessible fixings make the location of underlying structures difficult. They are also frequently found in non-standard sizes, preventing standard bracket solutions. Where the underlying structure includes a continuous wooden decking, brackets intended for battens may not adequately fit. A partial re-roof may be required to allow good practice insertion of appropriate zinc or lead flashing with custom brackets.

Double lap small clay tiles are also common in the UK and can be exceptionally hard, yet brittle. The close spacing and thinness of battens also creates problems with bracket insertion. Good practice for this type of roof would inevitably require use of flashing.

The use of stainless steel threaded studding passing through the roof covering and fixed to rafters is another method that lifts the weight of the collector off the tiles and has the advantage of independence from the tile construction.

To cope with the large variety of roof coverings, the use of a wide range of brackets, flexilbe sealants and custom flashings will often be required. See Figure 8.2 and also Section 8.4.2.

8.4.5   Lightning

According to BS 6651, lightning protection is normally only required where the assessed risk is greater than 1 in 100,000. The assessment considers soil type, trees, ground shape, size and vulnerability of the structure itself.

9.   Commissioning

9.1   Introduction

Commissioning can be defined as the advancement of an installation from the state of static completion to full working order to the specified requirements. It includes the setting to work of an installation, the regulation of the system and the fine tuning of the system. Commissioning includes recording all relevant measurements, flow rates and test results, and includes the preperation and submission of a commissioning report or certificate.

The completion of commissioning is the point at which the responsibility for the installed equipment is passed to the end-user. This may be different from a change of legal ownership. A commissioning certificate shall be provided as required by the client and relevant regulations. The key operational safety and performance parameters on a checklist are confirmed as operational. A sample certificate is shown in Appendix E. The values and tolerances of any variable or adjustable parameters are entered to enable future service personnel, or the user, to verify performance and safety. There may be more than one certificate if individual items can function separately i.e. hot water vessels or electrical services. In England and Wales commissioning is frequently required by law under Part L of the Building Regulations.

A commissioning engineer must be a suitably qualified person who can personally testify by signature and date that the equipment has been properly installed and commissioned. Such a person should be suitably informed and instructed. Commissioning engineers should work to an approved code of practice recognised under Building Regulations, such as CIBSE Commissioning Code M, and be properly and regularly assessed by a competent authority to a high standard.

Where energy-monitoring equipment is fitted, such as heat meters or flow meters, then on-site sensor matching and calibration may also be required.

9.2   Commissioning procedure

During commissioning, a number of variable settings have to be adjusted and set that are critical to the reliability and performance of the system. These settings must be recorded on the certificate handed to the user and a copy kept by the commissioning person. It can not be assumed that a set of individual components will correctly operate within the manufacturer's tolerances when simply assembled straight out of their boxes. Commissioning can help identify installation errors, such blockages or constrictions in circulation, incorrect flow/return orientation or incorrect wiring, but also correctly adapts the system to its individual location.

The procedure for commissioning a solar system is different compared to traditional heat sources in that the source of heat, the sun, being variable in nature, may not have heated the system up to temperature at the intended time of commissioning. Unless special procedures and equipment are used, commissioning of the primary system may have to be left until the sun becomes available to heat it up. In all cases, it is most desirable to commission on a bright or sunny day with the collector temporarily covered and the primary system and dedicated solar storage both cool. Careful consideration will have to be given to the means of fixing any temporary covers particularly in windy conditions and a safe means of access to the collector position provided.

In the case of a sealed, fully filled system, the adjustment of the pre-charge is decided by using Section 7.13 or the calculation method shown in Appendix D. The system side of the vessel should be at atmospheric pressure during the adjustment. The gas side is adjusted using a pressure gauge accurate to BS EN 837-1. In the event that the vessel gas needs to be re-filled, a typical tyre foot pump may suffice although the manufacturer of the vessel may require moisture reduction or nitrogen to reduce corrosion risk.

The fluid to be used in the primary systems is now prepared. It is desirable that this fluid is de-oxygenated (de-gassed) and de-ionised to avoid soluble oxygen boiling out upon being heated, which may cause circulation loss or corrosion as well as limescale deposition. In the event that the solar system does not heat up during the intended day of commissioning, the use of a de-gassed fluid would be essential to avoid a re-visit. Where antifreeze solutions are used, a method of confirming the concentration of glycol is required, typically using a refractometer. Further checks of acidity may be made to confirm the anti-corrosion qualities of an inhibited glycol solution. The use of purpose made, pre-mixed inhibited specialist antifreeze for solar systems sold in de-gassed sealed containers is strongly recommended. Before filling, consideration of flushing to clean the system, should be given according to BS 7593 however no chemical residues should be left that may react with the final filling fluid and care should be taken where there is a risk of freezing.

Providing the collector is cool, the system can be filled up to the desired cold system pressure deduced from Section 7.13 or the calculation method shown in Appendix D. For drain back systems see Section 7.14 or the calculation methods shown in Appendix D. In all cases, unnecessary air should now be removed from the primary system and the system pressure or level re-checked. In the case of a fully filled, sealed system the air removal is achieved in combination with the assistance of a circulation pump, system pressure gauge and air vents. The check valves may be temporarily disabled during this period. It is vital that all gas is removed before completing the commissioning and that no air vent is left without a closed isolating valve. A specialised high flow-rate commissioning pump and particulate filter may be required to adequately remove all gases in a fully-filled, sealed system at the same time as removing internal pipe debris. For a drain back system, a level indicator in the side of the vessel is used with the pump off, so that any over-fill is allowed to drip out into a temporary container. In all cases, the over-pressure control is briefly manually operated to confirm operation and safe discharge.

Once the electrical isolation and over-current protection is checked, the system pump and controls are now energised. The maximum circulation rate is temporarily enabled by manually over-ridding the pump controls then adjusting the pump speed selector. A circulation meter (flow meter) is used to monitor and set the desired rate, see Section 6.1.4. The adjustment of the pump control is now made including the switching differential, maximum store temperature and variable speed options see Section 6.1.3 and Appendix C. Sensors are checked to be correctly wired, in the correct locations, securely fixed and giving sensible readings. The location and operation of the back-up heat source thermostats and safety controls should be confirmed. Checks on circulation and system pressure are again made to ensure complete air removal, or in the case of drain back systems evidence of drain back through careful listening and observing fluid through the flow meter.

Once circulation is assured and all safety controls are engaged on automatic, any temporary covers over the collector are now removed and the system is allowed to heat up. Any multiple circuits are now checked for balancing through equal temperature distribution. Sensible operation of the system is now observed.

Final checks should include checking that all electrical covers are replaced, all pipe insulation intact, weatherproofing is in place, all air vents/level indicators isolated and drain-points secured against accidental opening. All adjustable settings are now recorded on the commissioning certificate along with additional administrative data.

10. User information

10.1 Introduction

Information relevant to the future owners of solar water heating equipment must be left on site. This should be in a dry, accessible, heat- and dust-free location, preferably adjacent to the pre-heat store or pump controller.

The information should include:

- Full system operation instructions
- User guide
- Maintenance schedule
- Decommissioning schedule
- Schematic diagram including location of key safety items
- Commissioning certificate
- Full record of dimensioning, performance, weather and load assumptions
- Contact details for specialised assistance
- BS 7671 certificate where relevant

10.2 Explaining the solar system to the customer

The operation of the solar water heating system must be fully explained to the end-user.

The general layout of the system should be explained including the location of the solar collector, store, pump, isolation valves and the controls. The relationship of the operation of the solar system to the back-up heat DHW source and any other uses of the solar heat should be covered. It should be pointed out that the solar heat is thermostatically interlinked with the back up heat source so that latter will only operate if its time controls are calling for heat and there is insufficient solar heat.

It should be explained that the supply of solar heat is intermittent and occurs in daylight hours mostly between spring and autumn or on any strong sunny day. It should be explained that the solar heat builds up slowly during the day and for some days it will not be sufficient for all the household's DHW demands. For this reason the back-up DHW heating must be kept operational to provide comfort at all times as well as minimising bacterial risks.

The end user should be shown where to electrically isolate the power supply to the solar system and informed that it should normally be left on to allow any safety features of the solar system to operate correctly and to allow the control functions to continue to display the temperatures around the system. This is the case even during periods of absence such as holidays. The end-user should be encouraged to explain to relevant visiting trades people that a solar hot water system is fitted and that some components within the insulation can become very hot. The locations of where users will find the operating instructions and contact details for further assistance should be shown.

On return from a period of absence such as a holiday, the DHW storage temperature may have reached its maximum and it should be explained that this temperature is adjustable, where it can be adjusted and what setting it has been set to. Where the system is designed to provide space heating, this should be clearly explained.

The maintenance schedule and the division of responsibilities between any end user inspections and intervention by a suitably qualified person should be explained.

11. Troubleshooting

The main reasons why some solar water heating systems perform poorly and malfunction are:

● frost damage to the collector due to degradation of antifreeze

● temperature sensors displaced from the correct position

● circulating pump seizure

● loss of fluid due to open vent evaporation, or slow leakage of liquid through an automatic air vent

● sealed system expansion vessel incorrectly sized, positioned or adjusted

● sealed system expansion vessel has lost pre-charge

● drainback pipes not falling downwards

● drainback vessel over-filled

● safety valve damaged and letting by

● residue from overheated antifreeze blocking pipes

● limescale blocking the collector, pipes or heat exchanger

● temperature differential between storage and panel wrongly set within solar controller

● pump control missing or malfunctioning

● another heating appliance interfering with heat transfer within the DHW store

● missing or damaged insulation of pipes and store

● incorrect or damaged location of temperature sensors

● inadequate air removal from pipes or collector

● incorrect pump speed

● flow and return pipes to cylinder and/or collector having the wrong orientation

If there is a significant drop in primary pressure or fluid level, suspect one or more of the following:

● overheating may have occurred during a period of hot weather if the circulation unintentionally failed or the system was incorrectly designed. When thermal energy is not being removed from the collector, the water temperature will rise and the water volume and system pressure could increase beyond safety device limits. In some types of system, this could result in the release of hot water or steam from the pressure relief valve or the automatic/manual vent. When the system returns to normal operating conditions, the pressure will reduce due to the loss in fluid volume.

- if there is a leak in the system, it may require a drain down and repair/replacement of the faulty component(s).

12. Maintenance

Solar water heating primary systems will benefit from annual inspection checks. Manufacturers and installers must provide instructions for the inspection checks, at handover. The minimum competency, test equipment or other requirements for an inspection, should be clearly stated in the information provided at handover.

An example list of items to be checked as part of a solar heating system visual inspection list could include the following:

- collector glazing is undamaged

- where visible, absorber paintwork or coating is sound

- the roof fixings are firm and the roof covering satisfactory

- fluid levels in the cistern, drainback or expansion vessel are checked against the specified levels

- pressure levels are checked against the specified levels

- electrical controls and temperature sensors are operating correctly

- the circulating pump is operating without due noise

- pipework insulation is firmly in place

- there are no condensation or damp spots, particularly around the pipework and fixings in the roof space

- all safety and information labels are in place.

Critical safety devices such as over-pressure safety valves and storage temperature limitation sensors are likely to require skilled checks and intervention no less than every 5 years. It should be noted that some associated storage and back-up heat sources may require safety checks annually.

For fully filled systems, an important item to be checked is the quality and quantity of antifreeze. This should be tested at least every five years, for system pressure, glycol concentration and acidity. This is done with a small refractometer and pH strips available from specialist solar antifreeze suppliers, as well as by observing the pressure gauge against the commissioned settings. Some antifreeze products also require regular replacement. The gas side of the expansion vessel should also be checked against commissioned settings noting this can only be done with the vessel isolated hence great care should be taken during sunny conditions.

Drainback systems also require the fluid to be checked but if containing plain water, then evidence of corrosion should be checked by way of extracting a small sample.

Regular de-scaling of the secondary side of the solar store may be required in high limescale deposit areas, especially at the heat exchanger surfaces. Where a direct solar system is found, regular de-scaling of the solar primary circuit is likely to be required as well as power or chemical flushing of sludge and disinfection of bacterial growth. However, if contamination or infestation is suspected, then consideration of a conversion to an indirect circuit should be considered.

13.   Health and safety considerations

A well-designed solar system should be installed and commisioned by a suitably qualified person. However, poor design or inadequate installation can be hazardous and expose people to unacceptable risks.

Installation work for solar water heating involves a sequence of tasks. One person may carry out all of these or each task may be the responsibility of a specialist member of a team. Installation may, for example, be subdivided into the traditional trades of plumbing, electrical, roofwork and access work. A heating engineer, conversant with the associated back-up heating appliances and local water quality issues, is generally required to commission a solar domestic water heating primary system and its storage. Engineers working with gas fired equipment must be registered with CORGI. For oil fired equipment they should be registered with OFTEC. The building control body will require notification of a solar water heating installation on buildings and minimum equipment requirements may apply.

A suitably qualified individual intending to carry out all the installing tasks will possess a high level of technical knowledge, physical fitness, familiarity with the tools of the trade and will have been formally trained and examined in his or her field of experience. A person intending to commission a solar water heating system will also be experienced in the design and/or installation of solar heating installations.

Whilst a business or enterprise consisting of a group of suitably qualified individuals might meet the requirements to install, a DIY person, working without the close supervision of a suitably qualified person on site, would almost certainly not be.

Method statement / Risk assessment

A method statement/risk assessment must be completed before work starts. This will cover construction, water quality and bacterial risks. An assessment of risks to workers, householders, members of the public and animals cannot be made unless a suitably qualified person visits the site. Such an inspection is different from a technical survey. The latter may be possible to complete away from the site, particularly if a new building is involved.

An inexperienced observer would be unlikely to fully anticipate the complexities and variables affecting solar heating that are found throughout the UK and Ireland. There are also unique risks involved in the installation of solar domestic hot water heating that should not be underestimated. The Management of Health & Safety at Work Regulations 1999 prescribes the minimum necessary actions. The law requires employers to appoint one or more suitably qualified persons to assist them in identifying and implementing the preventive and protective measures required.

Appendix A   Directives, Regulations and Standards

A1   England and Wales Regulations particularly relevant for water heating equipment without combustion

Regulation	Website	Notes
Water Supply (Water Fittings) Regulations 1999	www.wras.co.uk	Applies to all fittings in contact with the utilities' supply of water. Responsibility for compliance lies with the householder and installer, although certain approved contractors can issue certificates of compliance that provide immunity from prosecution to the householder. All solar water heating work is normally notifiable to the water utility and permission must be awaited for ten days, except when installed in extensions or if alterations of water systems in existing houses. Water (over 15 litres) must not be stored in domestic premises above 100°C, while avoidance of water contamination and undue consumption is mandatory. There are requirements for protection from freezing, use of certified fittings, methods of pipe fixing, safety devices on water stores plus extra requirements for non-metallic fittings. Note that different rules apply in Scotland, Northern Ireland and Republic of Ireland – see section A2.
The Pressure Equipment Regulations (PED) 1999	www.eurodyn.com	Applies where the equipment could hold pressures in excess of 0.5 bar above atmospheric under any foreseeable circumstances. Applies to the manufacturer (where placed on the market as a functional assembly) or else the commissioning engineer. Requires equipment to be safe and either to a sound engineering practice or CE-marked to a higher safety requirement. Where an attached system can overheat according to BS EN 12976, the collector is categorised as a steam generator.
The Building Regulations Part L 2006	www.communities.gov.uk	Applies to the conservation of heat and power in all new build, extensions and existing dwellings. Particularly affects replacement of hot water storage vessels and accompanying controls. All solar water heating work normally involving additional hot water storage is therefore notifiable to a building control officer unless a competent person can self-certify and issue a commissioning certificate. Requires minimum levels for insulation, time and temperature controls for hot water storage. Also, water storage vessels to have a minimum performance. A commissioning certificate or similar provision is required to be left. Note that different rules apply in Scotland, Northern Ireland and Republic of Ireland – see section A2.
The Building Regulations Part G3 2000	www.communities.gov.uk	Applies to hygiene in buildings, particularly unvented hot water storage. Requires that only competent operatives should install such approved equipment along with associated safety equipment.
The Building Regulations Part P 2005	www.communities.gov.uk	Applies to any electrical work that involves adding new circuits to dwellings and any work in special locations such as kitchens, bathrooms, swimming pools and photovoltaic power. A competent person must either do the work or certify the work to a building control body. There are certain exceptions; it is permitted to add or replace outlets to existing circuits in non-special locations. All work should comply with, and further details may be found, in BS 7671:2001.
Control of Substances Hazardous to Health Regulations (COSHH) 1994	www.hse.gov.uk	Require employers to assess the risks from hazardous substances and take appropriate precautions. This requires precautions to reduce legionella poisoning.
Regulation 7	www.communities.gov.uk	Materials and workmanship. Building work shall be carried out – (a) with adequate and proper materials which: (i) are appropriate for the circumstances in which they are used, (ii) are adequately mixed or prepared, and (iii) are applied, used or fixed so as adequately to perform the functions for which they are designed; and (b) in a workmanlike manner.

IMPORTANT: Please turn over for an explanation of the summary of Regulations shown above.

Important information relating to A1

A simplified interpretation of some common regulations is shown above. They are provided in good faith and should not be taken as the full meaning of the law. Any actions intended to be based on the law should refer to copies of published legislation typically available from The Stationery Office or be based on advice from a qualified practitioner of law. This text is of a general nature only and is not intended to address the specific circumstances of any particular individual or entity. It is not necessarily comprehensive, complete, accurate or up to date. Note that a 'manufacturer' of a solar water heating system can on occasions be considered the commissioning engineer, particularly where custom components are being assembled. NB: For regional variations, please refer to A2.

A2   Country variations of regulations where known to differ from A1

Scotland	
Water Byelaws 2000 (Scotland)	www.wras.org.uk
Building (Scotland) Regulations 2004 as ammended in 2006	www.sbsa.gov.uk

Northern Ireland	
No known equivalent to Water Supply and Fitting Regulations	www.dfpni.gov.uk
Building Regulations (Northern Ireland) 2000 Statutory rules of Northern Ireland 2000 No. 38	www.dfpni.gov.uk

Republic of Ireland	
No known equivalent to Water Supply and Fitting Regulations	www.environ.ie
The Building Regulations 1997 - 2006	www.environ.ie

A3   EU Directives

Further details available from: www.europa.eu.int

Construction Products Directive: 89/106/EEC Construction Products Regulations 1991 S1 1620	Requires that products produced for incorporation in a permanent manner in construction works are to be fit for the intended use. This would particularly apply to solar collectors in respect of the following:· ● mechanical resistance and stability ● safety in case of fire ● hygiene, health and the environment ● safety in use ● protection against noise ● energy economy
Electromagnetic Compatability Directive: 89/336/EEC E.M.C. Regulations 1992 S1 2372 as amended by 1995 S1 3180, 2006 S1 1449 E.M.C. (Amendments)	Requires that equipment be not degraded by an electromagnetic phenomenon. If an apparatus, when used as intended, does not degrade the performance of others in its electromagnetic environment, both present and foreseeable, it should be considered compliant with the essential requirement of the Directive. Particularly applies to both AC and DC pumps and controls that may interfere with radio signals. Compliance is demonstrated by a CE mark on a pump or control.
Low voltage Directive: 73/23/EEC L.V. Electrical Equipment (Safety) Regulations 1989 S1 728	Applies to all electrical equipment designed for use with a voltage rating of between 50 and 1000 V alternating current. Particularly would cover pumps or controller in solar heating systems. It takes in health aspects of noise and vibrations, and ergonomic aspects of electrical equipment. This may be placed on the market only if, having been constructed in accordance with good engineering practice in safety matters, it does not endanger the safety of persons, domestic animals or property when properly installed and maintained and used in applications for which it was made. Where machinery has an electricity supply, it must be designed, constructed and equipped so that all hazards of an electrical nature are, or can be, prevented.
Machinery Directive: 98/37/EC	Applies to assemblies of linked parts or components, at least one of which moves, with the appropriate actuators, control and power circuits, etc, joined together for a specific application. May apply to solar water heating particularly when motor valve linkages are involved.

A simplified interpretation of some common directives is shown above. They are provided in good faith and should not be taken as the full meaning of the law. Any actions intended to be based on the law should refer to copies of published legislation typically available from The European Commission in Brussels. This text is of a general nature only and is not intended to address the specific circumstances of any particular individual or entity. It is not necessarily comprehensive, complete, accurate or up to date. Note that a 'manufacturer' of a solar water heating system can on occasions be considered the commissioning engineer, particularly where custom components are being assembled. Dates correct at time of publication.

A4   UK Regulations particularly relevant for construction

Further details available from: www.hse.gov.uk

Health & Safety At Work Act (HSW) 1974	Reporting of Injuries, Diseases and Dangerous Occurrences Regulations (RIDDOR) 1995
Management Health & Safety at Work Regulations (MHSWR) 1999	Noise at Work Regulations 1989
Work at Height Regulations 2005	Electricity at Work Regulations 1989
Construction Regulations (Head Protection) 1989	Control of Substances Hazardous to Health Regulations (COSHH) 1994
New Construction (Design and Management) Regulations (CDM) 2007	Personal Protective Equipment at Work Regulations 1992
Lifting Operations and Lifting Equipment Regulations (LOLER) 1998	Confined Spaces Regulations 1997
Manual Handling Operations Regulations 1992	The Workplace (Health, Safety and Welfare) Regulations 1992 (WHSWA)
Provision and Use of Work Equipment Regulations (PUWER) 1998	Health and Safety (First Aid) Regulations 1981

A simplified interpretation of some common regulations is shown above. They are provided in good faith and should not be taken as the full meaning of the law. Any actions intended to be based on the law should refer to copies of published legislation typically available from The Stationery Office or be based on advice from a qualified practitioner of law. This text is of a general nature only and is not intended to address the specific circumstances of any particular individual or entity. It is not necessarily comprehensive, complete, accurate or up to date and there may be variations outside England and Wales.

A5   Solar standards

BS 7431:1991	Method for assessing solar water heaters. Elastomeric materials for absorbers, connecting pipes and fittings
BS 6785:1986	Code of practice for solar heating systems for swimming pools
prEN 12977-1:2005	Thermal solar systems and components. Custom built systems. General requirements
prEN 12977-2:2005	Thermal solar systems and components. Custom built systems. Test methods
prEN 12977-3:2005	Performance characterisation of stores for solar heating systems
BS EN ISO 9488:2000	Solar energy. Vocabulary
BS EN 12976-1:2006	Thermal solar systems and components. Factory made systems. General requirements
BS EN 12976-2:2006	Thermal solar systems and components. Factory made systems. Test methods
BS EN 12975-1:2006	Thermal solar systems and components. Solar collectors. General requirements
BS EN 12975-2:2006	Thermal solar systems and components. Solar collectors. Test methods
BS 5918	Code of practice for solar heating systems for domestic hot water

Note a prEN document is not a European Standard. It is distributed for review and comments. It is subject to change without notice. The documents in this section are generally available from British Standards Institute.

A6   Other relevant standards

BS 476-3:2004	Fire test on building materials and structures. Classification and method of test for external fire exposure to roofs.
BS 1566-1:2002	Copper indirect cylinders for domestic purposes. Open vented copper cylinders. Requirements and test methods
BS 4814:1990	Specification for expansion vessels using an internal diaphragm, for sealed hot water heating systems
BS 5422	Methods of specifying thermal insulation materials on pipes, ductwork and equipment in the temperature range of -40°C to 700°C.
BS 5449:1990	Specification of forced circulation hot water central heating systems for domestic premises
BS 5970:2001	Code of practice for thermal insulation of pipes and equipment
BS 6701:2004	Telecommunications equipment and telecommunications cabling. Specification for installation, operation and maintenance
BS 6700:2006	Specification and design, installation, testing and maintenance of services supplying water for domestic uses within buildings and their curtilages
BS 6920 (all parts)	Suitability of non-metallic products for use in contact with water intended for human consumption with regard to their effect on the quality of the water
BS 7074-1:1989	Application, selection and installation of expansion vessels and ancillary equipment for sealed water systems. Code of practice for domestic heating and hot water supply
BS 7206:1990	Specification for unvented hot water storage units and packages
BS 7671:2001	Requirements for electrical installations. IEE Wiring Regulations. Sixteenth edition
BS 8000-15:1990	Workmanship on building sites. Code of practice for hot and cold water services (domestic scale)
BS EN 12828:2003	Heating systems in buildings. Design for water-based heating systems
BS EN 12831:2003	Heating systems in buildings. Method for calculation of the design heat load
BS 6399 (all parts)	Loadings for Buildings

A7   Other CIBSE Domestic Building Services Panel Publications

Domestic heating design guide

Underfloor heating design and installation guide

A8   CORGI Publications

Essential gas safety

A9   HVCA Publications

TR20	Installation and testing of pipework systems Part 4 Hot water service
DCH/1	Domestic central heating installation specification
JS/1	Worksafe Guide to Site Safety
JS/23	Risk Management Manual

A10 IPHE Publications

Plumbing engineering services guide

A11 OFTEC Publications

| Technical information book 3 | Installation requirements for oil fired equipment |
| Technical information book 4 | System design and operating principles |

A12 References

CIBSE Minimising the risk of Legionnaires' disease TM13 Year ISBN: 1903287235

HSC Approved Code of Practice and Guidance L8 Control of legionella bacteria in water systems 2000. ISBN 0717617726

WRAS Water Regulations guidance 2nd Edition 2000 ISBN 0953970809

DTI Pressure equipment – Guidance notes on the UK regulations April 2005 URN 05/1074

Appendix B   Glossary

Absorber	Component of collector which absorbs solar radiation
Aperture area	Area of opening through which unconcentrated solar radiation is admitted
Auxiliary heat source	Back-up heat other than solar to supplement the output of the solar energy system
Closed loop	A closed circuit where the fluid is recirculated
Cold feed	Start of the incoming water supply to a system
Collector	Absorbs solar radiation and transfers thermal energy to fluid passing through it
Collector efficiency	Ratio of energy removed by transfer fluid to incident solar radiation
Collector loop	Circuit that includes the collector, pump, pipes and exchanger for transferring heat
Combi-boilers	Boilers that provide DHW and space heating
Combi-stores	Combination of DHW and space heating storage
Combined storage	A single vessel that includes heat sources other than solar
Commissioning engineer	Person responsible for declaring a fitted system is fit for purpose and safe
Conduction	Movement of heat in solid
Convection	Movement of heat in a fluid
DHW	Domestic hot water consumed in the dwelling
Differential temperature controller	(DTC) Compares two temperatures which may vary independently
Direct system	Where the heated water that is to be consumed passes through the collector
Downstream	Direction with the movement of water
Drainback	A system that automatically fills and refills the primary fluid into the collector
Draindown	Where a direct system drains the primary contents to waste
DTC - Differential Thermostat Control	Switches on equipment by comparing two varying temperatures
ELV (Extra Low Voltage)	Electricity that is sub 50 V AC or ripple-free 120 V DC
Evacuated collector	Where the space between the absorber and cover is evacuated
Flat plate collector	Where the absorber surface is essentially planar
Flow	The part of a circuit which is hot from the heat source
Fully -filled	A system normally above atmospheric pressure with all air removed
Gross collector area	Maximum projected area of complete collector excluding any integral mounting brackets and pipework
Hydraulically secure	All fluid contents contained within the system in all conditions, without release to the atmosphere
Indirect system	Where a heat transfer fluid other than the consumed water passes through the collector
Installer	Assembles and fits components into a system. Equivalent to a manufacturer where the assembly is customised
Interlock	A means of control wiring which prevents a device from operating unnecessarily
Irradiation	Electromagnetic energy incident per unit area
Load	Amount of energy or power required from a system
Manufacturer	Produces components and assembly kits
Net absorber area	Maximum projected area of an area reached by solar radiation
Open vented system	Where there is contact by the heat transfer fluid to the atmosphere via a vent pipe and cistern
Parasitic losses	Energy consumed by pumps, fans and controls during operation
Peak power	The maximum rate of energy flow
Pre-heat vessel	A contained body of fluid which accepts heat prior to heating by an back-up heat source
Return	The part of the circuit that is cool to the heat source
SDHW	Solar heated Domestic Hot Water
Sealed system	(Closed and unvented). Where the system is sealed from the atmosphere
Selective	A surface whose optical properties are wave-length dependent
Solar fraction	Energy supplied by the solar system divided by the total system load
Stagnation	Status of a collector or system when no heat being removed by the transfer fluid
Standing losses	Energy consumed by equipment continuously irrespective of operation
Stratification	Natural layering of fluids of different densities
Switching point	Where a control creates an event based on a varying parameter
Thermo-siphon system	Utilises only water density changes to achieve circulation
Upstream	Direction against the movement of water
Useful energy	The solar energy, after losses, that reaches the appliances
Utilisation factor	Factor of time delay and the quantity of surplus

Appendix C Features frequently found on solar DTC's

NB: Not all features indicated are available on all controllers. Some indicated optional features should be used with caution when used on DHW storage due to scalding risks

Abbreviation	Description	Notes
TCol	Readout of collector temperature	No adjustment. Part of the Delta T control.
TLow	Readout of solar storage or heat exchanger temperature	No adjustment. Part of the Delta T control or limiting store temperature.
THigh	Readout of supplementary storage temperature	No adjustment. For information or limiting store temperature.
Delta T On	Adjustment of switch-on of store loading pump	The difference between TCol and TLow
Delta T Off	Adjustment of switch-off of store loading pump	This may be referred to as hysterisis of Delta T On.
StMax	Adjustment of maximum storage limit, switching off the store loading pump. Auto reset.	Usually uses TLow but Thigh is also possible.
Time	Adjustment of time clock	Used for anti-legionella control and thermostatic options.
ColMax	Adjustment of collector maximum limit, switching off the store loading pump. Auto reset.	Once engaged, may lead to rapid stagnation of the collector hence may lead to long periods of no solar gain until the collector next cools. Overrides Delta T On.
SysCool	Optional adjustment of StMax to allow switching on of another relay to allow the movement of heat out of the solar store. Auto reset.	Helps avoid risk of long periods of stagnation in case that ColMax engages for heating a second store or dumping heat. Can also use Thigh.
ReCool	Option for switching on the store loading pump when StMax is exceeded	Helps avoid risk of long periods of stagnation by running solar pump. Temporarily overrides StMax to higher limit and then cools store after sundown. Temporarily overrides Delta T Off. May not be compatible with Building regulation G3 in England and Wales and may cause nuisance tripping of other limit thermostats.
MinPump	Adjustment of lowest speed of store loading pump	Requires a semi-conductor relay capable of pulsed output of the store loading pump. Varies according to the difference between TCol and TLow in order to achieve a steady difference usually around 10 K. Typical range 30-100%.
ColMin	Adjustment of collector minimum limit, switching off store loading pump	Can assist preventing condensation on pipes. Overrides Delta T On.
TubeCol	Option for switching on the store loading pump for short fixed period according to rising rate of TCol	Suitable for where the sensor for TCol is unfavourably located perhaps during the passing of temporary shading or certain tube collector designs. Overrides Delta T Off.
OverRide	Option of switching the store loading pump on, off or automatically.	Normally left on automatic unless the system is being serviced or commissioned.
Error	Readout of implausible event	May be auto reset or manual reset. Can indicate a broken sensor or stagnation.
Thermostat	Option for switching on a second relay according to THigh	Independent of primary store loading pump. Can be used for store cooling or additional heating.
OpHours	Readout of pump run hours	Useful for fault finding, nocturnal heat loss and determining service intervals
Frost protection	Optional adjustment of collector minimum threshold, switching on the store loading pump up to a pre-set upper limit. Auto reset.	Inadvisable to use in UK and Ireland due to excessive thermal and electrical losses.
HeatCalc	Readout of energy calculation according to adjusted circulation rate, flow & return temperatures	Can use pre-set circulation rate or measurement of a pulse-counter flowmeter.
Bypass	Option for switching on a second relay according to the difference between TCol and a supplementary sensor	Second relay can operate a pump or a motor valve. Store loading pump does not operate simultaneously of second pump. Temporarily overrides Delta T On.
LightSensor	Option for switching on a second relay according to the light levels	Second relay can operate a pump or a motor valve. Store loading pump does not operate simultaneously of second pump. Temporarily overrides Delta T On.
Legionella Switch	Option for switching on a second relay according to maximum temperature of THigh or TLow within 24 period	Second relay usually controls either a secondary circulating pump or supplementary heat source to ensure store reaches 60 C. daily. The time period is sometimes adjustable.

Appendix D Detailed calculation of expansion vessel settings

A more accurate calculation for expansion vessel sizes follows below. This is particularly required for larger system designs or where doubt otherwise exists.

The first step is to determine the volume of fluid in the primary system, (V_{total}). This is the sum of the total volume in the collectors, plus the heat exchange coil, plate exchangers if present plus the interconnecting pipework. Reputable equipment manufacturers will supply the correct figures for their products although some examples are given in see Section 7.13. Next, the amount that volume will expand when heated is calculated. The eight boxes in this Appendix show the calculation in sequence with key results highlighted.

Where there exists insufficient volume (i.e. pipe distance) between the collectors and the expansion vessel, then an intermediate auxiliary vessel must be used in order to prevent the possibility that steam or vaporised fluid may strike the rubber membrane. The preference is for more than 50% of the fluid between the collector and the expansion vessel to exceed the 'working' volume of the system i.e. the expected movement of fluid into the expansion vessel during stagnation. This is frequently not met where an expansion vessel is located in the roof void behind the collector. The intermediate auxiliary vessel could be in effect a large diameter pipe but could also be a purpose designed steel vessel. Where such a vessel is required to be sized, it can be done so either as equal to the working volume or 7% of the total system volume when hot, whichever is larger.

Calculation of expansion vessel sizes for solar DHW systems is different to that for ordinary central heating systems due to the greater temperature range that the expansion vessel is required to accept. The greater height difference and pressure, the use of glycol antifreeze and the likelihood of vaporisation of fluid in the solar collector during stagnation also have to be allowed for. The moment of vaporisation in the collector strongly depends on the pressure in the system and the temperature and properties of the fluid. This moment can be pre-determined by design of the above variables using tables in this book.

A moment's care should be given to consider the difference of absolute and relative pressures. Most discussed pressures in system design are in reference to atmospheric pressure at sea level. Here a pressure gauge will be adjusted to read zero, even though the absolute pressure can be considered approximately 1 Bar. There is normally no problem in consistently using the gauge pressure measurements within the confines a solar system. However, particular care should be given where calculating measurements in an expansion vessel due to the relative interaction of the rubber membrane and pre-pressurised gas. Where absolute pressure is used, it is customary to add 1 Bar to the gauge pressure in these circumstances.

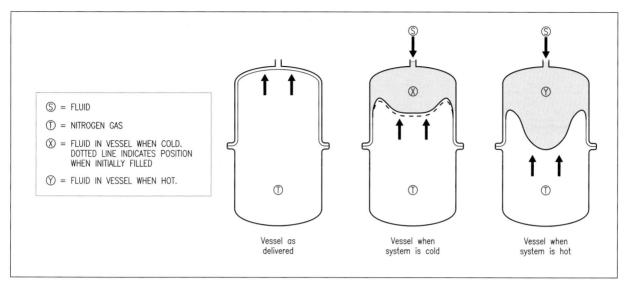

Figure D.1 Construction and operation of an expansion vessel

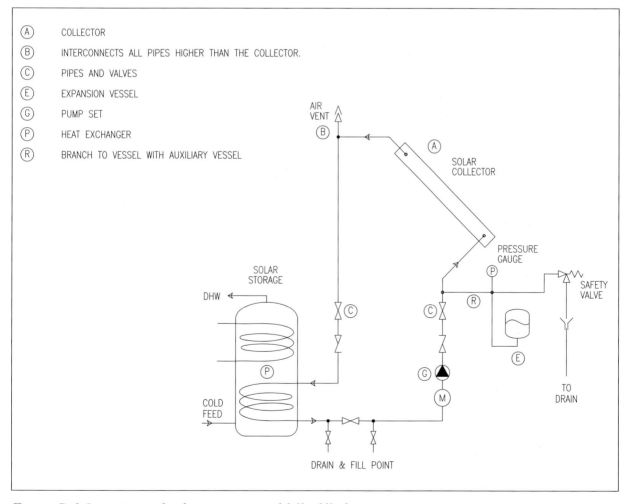

Figure D.2 Locations of volume content of fully filled system

Volume	Abbreviation	Key in diagrams
Volume in collector	$V_{collector}$	A
Volume interconnects and pipes higher than collector	$V_{interconnects}$	B
Volume all pipes on branch to expansion vessel including auxiliary vessels but not vessel itself	V_{branch}	R
Volume all pipes in circuit below collector, pumps	V_{pipes}	C & G
Volume heat exchangers	$V_{exchanger}$	P
Water seal present inside vessel at a minimum in cold conditions to protect membrane from steam, avoid under pressure and accommodate micro leaks.	V_{wseal}	X
Volume of movement of fluid in vessel in all working conditions	$V_{working}$	Y
Nominal size of expansion vessel	$V_{nominal}$	E

Table D.1 Glossary of terms used in calculating system volume diagrams

Term	Abbreviation	Calculations
Volume increase of fluid when heated	$V_{expanded}$	$= Y - X$
Volume of liquid in entire system when cold not including the expansion vessel	V_{total}	$= V_{collector} + V_{interconnects} + V_{branch} + V_{pipes} + V_{exchanger}$
Volume of vapour formed after full evaporation	V_{vapour}	$= V_{collector} + V_{interconnects}$

Table D.2 Glossary of terms used in calculating system volume calculations

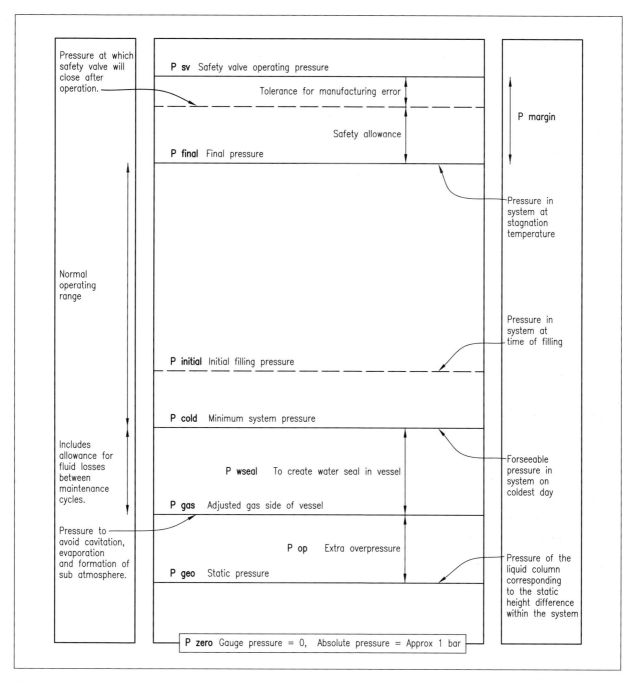

Figure D.3 Pressure levels

1.   Calculating the volume of expansion

The amount by which the total volume will expand, $V_{expanded}$, is considered at the worst case of the temperature difference, typically between the evaporation point at which the circulation ceases and the coldest average system temperature. It is reasonable to assume a temperature difference between 4°C to over 140°C.

A figure of 8% expansion is used for both plain water and an aqueous glycol mixture across the whole temperature range.

2.   Volume of extra fluid for steam protection and leak reservoir

The expansion vessel is partly-filled with sufficient fluid to act as a reservoir able to overcome the contraction of water at any lower temperatures than applied on the day of filling the system and as a potential micro leaks. It also serves to protect the rubber membrane from steam that could damage it. This is achieved by sufficient over-pressurisation of the system when cold. Assuming a worst case between filling at 20°C and operating at a temperature as low as -24°C, then the volume of the accommodation (V_{wseal}) for water/glycol expansion is calculated as:

$$V_{wseal} = V_{total} \times Coeff \times (20 + 24)$$

Where Coeff is the average expansion coefficient of the fluid = 0.000654.

This is approximately 3% of the initial collector circuit volume. However, considering smaller systems, it is recommended that V_{wseal} should not be less than 3 litres in any case to allow for some slow de-pressurisation over time and as a 'plug' to prevent steam reaching the flexible membrane.

3.   The working and extra vapour volume created upon vaporisation

The vapour volume V_{vapour} is equal to the sum of the volume of liquid in the collector array plus the volume of the pipework adjacent to the collectors that it is considered might vaporisation particularly during stagnation. Liquid in any pipework at the same level or above the collectors is likely to vaporise in strong sunlight without circulation hence, it is best to err on the side of caution and over-estimate the fluid volume at vaporisation. Note that some collectors have poor 'emptying' behaviour during the vaporisation phase.

The required usable working volume of the expansion vessel, $V_{working}$, will be:

$$V_{working} = V_{expanded} + V_{wseal} + V_{vapour}$$

4. **Deciding the safety allowance and margin of error for final expected system pressure during stagnation**

The response pressure of the safety valve, P_{sv}, is a 'red-line' limit that should not be intentionally reached during any predictable operating condition in order to retain the system contents. In practice, in domestic solar water heating systems, safety valve response pressures of 3 Bar (300kPa) or 6 Bar (600kPa) are mainly used, as these ratings are easily available.

A safety allowance and margin of manufacturing error should be created between 'red-line' pressure limit and the designed maximum operational pressure, P_{final}, to prevent any response of the safety valve during all foreseeable operation conditions, especially during stagnation. A selection of P_{final} can also be used to set the intended vaporisation point of the antifreeze. By increasing the safety margin, for a given vessel volume size, the fluctuations between hot and cold system pressures are therefore reduced and the selection of P_{final} is kept lower. Alternatively, the nominal vessel size is increased to give less pressure swing for a given system.

The margin, P_{margin} is usually set at least 10% below that of the safety valve pressure P_{sv}, to achieve intrinsic security (no release of fluid upon stagnation), but in any case at least to 0.5 Bar (50kPa). This could be increased if the safety valve is located at the base of a tall system in sympathy with static head (see following box).

$$P_{margin} = 0.1 \text{ x } P_{sv} \qquad P_{margin} > 0.5 \text{ Bar (50kPa)}$$

From this, the final pressure, P_{final} i.e. the maximum anticipated operating pressure when hot, is derived:

$$P_{final} = P_{sv} - P_{margin}$$

5.   Setting the adjustable pre-charge of the gas side of the expansion vessel

The static height is the offset between the expansion vessel and the highest point of the collector circuit. The latter is usually defined by the upper edge of the collector or by the air vent. This water gauge (or geodetic) pressure P_{geo} is equivalent to the gravity pressure head, H_{geo}, of a water column of this height:

$$P_{geo} = H_{geo} \times 1Bar/10m$$

The desired overpressure, P_{op}, of the collector at the highest point in the circuit, is added to P_{geo} and provides a means to prevent pressures at high level in the system becoming sub-atmospheric in any conditions, which could lead to the suction of air into air vents or small micro leaks that would not normally loose liquid from the system. It is also a value that can be used to prevent pump cavitation dependant on its location in the system. A typical recommended value for small installations is 0.5 Bar, 50 kPa. If higher values of over-pressure are used, the less operating range becomes available for a given vessel volume size.

The relative gauge pressure above atmospheric pressure of the gas side of the expansion vessel, P_{gas}, can only be accurately set by the installer when the vessel is disconnected from the circuit. It is calculated by the designer using the sum of the water gauge height (geodetic pressure) ,P_{geo}, plus the desired amount of overpressure to be maintained in the collector field, P_{op}. As a purchased expansion vessel usually does not necessarily have the required level of pressurisation when new, it needs to be adjusted on site by either releasing or adding gas:

$$P_{gas} = P_{op} + P_{geo}$$

If the system pressure is only set at P_{gas}, then no fluid will enter the expansion vessel. The initial cold filling pressure, $P_{initial}$ should be raised above the level of P_{gas} , to push some fluid into the vessel against P_{gas} This provides an allowance for fluid losses between maintenance cycles and protects the expansion vessel membrane from potential jets of steam during some operational phases. This extra pressure is called P_{wseal} and the extra volume of liquid in the vessel it creates is called V_{wseal}.

6.   Additional pressure creating liquid safety seal in vessel

With the volume of the fluid 'reservoir', V_{wseal}, being determined from box 2, the extra pressure needed to create it, P_{wseal}, can now determined. The initial cold system operating pressure that pushes against the membrane from the liquid side of the expansion vessel, $P_{initial}$, is set to a value that will exceed the pre-charge gas pressure, P_{gas}, when cold. A typical value to achieve this is 0.3 Bar although it can be derived more accurately from Boyles law of physics related to the ratio of pressure change to volume change in the vessel. By applying P_{wseal} to the fluid system pressure, sufficient liquid is swapped from the solar circuit and into the vessel to create a liquid 'safety' seal.

$$P_{wseal} = 0.3 \text{ Bar}$$

7.   Initial filling pressure when cold

The initial cold filling pressure, $P_{initial}$ of the fluid in the solar circuit is set to the pre-charge gas pressure in the expansion vessel, P_{gas} plus the equivalent of the water reservoir, P_{wseal} :

$$P_{initial} = \frac{P_{wseal} + P_{gas}}{P_{wseal} + (P_{op} + P_{geo})}$$

8.   Calculating the vessel nominal size

The pressure factor, P_f, is obtained by taking the final pressure P_{final} plus atmospheric pressure, approximately 1 Bar, as measured at the expansion vessel, and dividing by the "operating pressure reserve", i.e. the offset between final and initial pressure, that defines the maximal contraction of the gas side. An allowance for the pump head P_{pump}, typically 0.3 Bar, is also made hence the pressure factor is:

$$P_f = \frac{P_{final} + 1 \text{ Bar}}{P_{final} - (P_{gas} + P_{pump})}$$

The nominal volume of the expansion vessel is not completely available to the system fluid as part of the vessel is filled with gas. The relationship between the usable, working and the nominal volume of the expansion vessel $V_{nominal}$ is determined as follows:

$$V_{nominal} = P_f \times V_{working}$$

The inverse of this equation for P_f is called the expansion vessel efficiency. In situations where the vessel is likely to be significantly affected by both liquid and ambient temperatures approaching those of the manufacturer's tolerances, then a 10% increase on the vessel size should be considered.

Worked example – 1

Assume a solar hot water system consisting of 6m² of solar collector with a collector circuit of 20m of 15mm diameter, 1mm wall thickness copper pipework. The heat transfer liquid is 60% water, 40% glycol. The system's heat exchange cylinder coil is 1.6m of 15mm finned tube. The expansion vessel is to be fitted 4.5 metres below the highest part of the solar collector and the safety valve intended to be at 3 bar pressure. The pump head upon stagnation is assumed at 0.5 Bar. It is intended to design the system to at least be hydraulically secure and withhold fluid upon stagnation.

Measured data from site	
Collector volume = 0.74 litres / m²	**4.44 litres**
Volume of pipework and heat exchanger	**2.87 litres**
Installation volume V_{total} = 4.44 + 2.87 litres	**7.31 litres**
Water gauge (Geodetic) altitude	**4.5 m**
Estimated vapour volume in pipes 4m from top of panel 2m from bottom	**0.8 litres**
Collector liquid displaced upon stagnation	**5.24 litres**

Table D.3 Data for worked examples

Calculations:

Nominal expansion coefficient	8.0%
(for 40% glycol, 60% water, 130°c temperature difference)	
Expansion volume $V_{expanded}$ $\quad$ = 0.080 x V_{total} =	0.59 l
Vessel 'water seal' set to minimum V_{wseal}	3.00 l
Vapour volume V_{vapour} $\quad$ = 4.44 + 0.80 =	5.24 l
Required working volume of expansion vessel	
$V_{working} = V_{expanded} + V_{wseal} + V_{vapour}$ $\quad$ = 0.59 + 3.00 + 5.24 =	8.83 l
Water gauge (geodetic) pressure P_{geo} @ 4.5m x 1 Bar /10m	0.45 Bar
Desired collector field pressurisation P_{op}	0.50 Bar
Gas side pre-charge of expansion vessel	
$P_{gas} = P_{geo} + P_{op}$ $\quad$ = 0.45 + 0.5 =	0.95 Bar

Response pressure of safety valve P_{sv} 3.00 Bar

Pressure margin for safe operation $P_{margin} = P_{sv}$ x 10%   0.30 Bar

However, 0.5 Bar should be considered the lowest hence $P_{margin} =$ 0.50 Bar

Note: A P_{final} of 2.5 Bar will cause a vaporisation point around 115°C.

Final or maximum operating pressure $P_{final} = P_{sv} - P_{margin} = 3.0 - 0.5 =$ 2.50 Bar

Pressure equivalent for water seal $P_{wseal} =$ 0.30 Bar

Pressure factor

$$P_f = \frac{P_{final} + 1 Bar}{P_{final} - (P_{gas} + P_{pump})} = \frac{2.50 + 1.00}{2.50 - (0.95 + 0.30)}$$

$$P_f = 3.50 / 1.25 = \mathbf{2.80}$$

Required nominal volume of expansion vessel

$V_{nominal} > P_f$ x $V_{working}$ = 2.80 x 8.83 =   24.72 l

Next available standard size of expansion vessel =   25.0 l

The initial filling pressure of system fluid $P_{initial} = P_{gas} + P_{wseal}$

$P_{initial} = 0.95 + 0.30$ 1.25 Bar

Worked example – 2

Same system as example above but with 6 bar safety limit valve P_{sv} and 1.5 Bar collector over pressure (P_{op})

Pressure margin for safe operation $P_{margin} = 10\% \ P_{sv}$ 0.60 Bar

Final or maximum operating pressure $P_{final} = P_{sv} - P_{margin}$ 5.40 Bar

Note: A P_{final} of 5.4 Bar will cause a vaporisation point exceeding 150°C which will reduce antifreeze durability. A P_{final} is instead chosen at 3.5 Bar which will allow antifreeze to vapourise at 135 C. This in effect increases the safety margin to over 40%.

Gas side pre-charge of expansion vessel

$$P_{gas} = P_{geo} + P_{op} = 0.45 + 1.5 =$$ 1.95 Bar

Pressure equivalent for water seal $P_{wseal} = 0.30$ Bar

Pressure factor

$$P_f = \frac{P_{final} + 1 Bar}{P_{final} - (P_{gas} + P_{pump})} = \frac{3.5 + 1.00}{3.5 - (1.95 + 0.30)}$$

$$P_f = 6.40 / 1.25 = \mathbf{2.03}$$

Required nominal volume of expansion vessel

$$V_{nominal} > P_f \times V_{working} = 3.6 \times 8.83 = \qquad 31.90 \ l$$

Next available size   =   40.0 litre

The initial filling pressure of system fluid $P_{initial} = P_{gas} + P_{wseal}$

$$P_{initial} = 1.95 + 0.30 \qquad\qquad 2.25 \ Bar$$

Appendix E   Detailed drainback vessel calculations

The calculation of sizing the drainback vessel starts, as with expansion vessels, with the total fluid volume of the system although in this case it is in two parts as the system also contains air, this being also considered a fluid as per all gases. These expand at greatly different rates and sometimes at different temperatures. A careful assessment of where the drainback level is when the pump is off will allow the split between air (V_{air}) and liquid (V_{liquid}) to be calculated as below, see also Section 7.14.

Care should be given to consider the difference of absolute and relative pressures. Most discussed pressures in system design are in reference to atmospheric pressure at sea level. Here a pressure gauge will be adjusted to read zero, even though the absolute pressure can be considered approximately 1 Bar. There is normally no problem in consistently using the gauge pressure measurements within the confines a solar system. However, particular care should be given where calculating measurements in a drainback system due to the sub atmosphere conditions frequently created at the top of the systems. Where absolute pressure is used, it is customary to add 1 Bar to the gauge pressure in these circumstances.

---

1.   Calculating the volume of expansion

A gas such as air will expand considerably more than a liquid such as water and acts a 'spring' to accommodate the liquid expansion as well as its own.

The amount by which the total liquid volume when filled, V_{liquid} will expand, $V_{expanded}$ is considered at the worst-case scenario, typically just at or after stagnation with the pump on. It is reasonable to assume a worst-case temperature difference between cold filling, say with water at 10°C and with an atmospheric stagnation at perhaps 95°C.

A figure of 4% expansion is used for both plain water and an aqueous glycol mixture across the whole temperature range.

This liquid expansion will cause the air to be compressed and the pressure will rise to a final design pressure P_{final}.

---

2.   Deciding the safety margin and finial expected system pressure during stagnation

The response pressure of the safety valve, P_{sv}, is a 'redline' danger limit that should not be intentionally reached during any predictable operating condition. In practice, in domestic solar water heating systems, safety valve response pressures of 3 Bar (300kPa) are mainly used for drainback.

A margin should be created between 'red-line' pressure limits and the maximum operational pressure to prevent any response of the safety valve during all foreseeable operation conditions.

The margin, P_{margin}, is usually set to 10% below that of the safety valve pressure, P_{sv}, but at least to 0.5 Bar (50kPa).

$$P_{margin} = 0.1 \times P_{sv} \qquad P_{margin} > 0.5 \text{ Bar (50kPa)}$$

From this, the final pressure, P_{final}, i.e. the maximum anticipated operating pressure when hot, is derived:

$$P_{final} = P_{sv} - P_{margin}$$

Typically, P_{final} will be less than 2.5 Bar.

3.   Calculation of the tidal (quiescent) volume

The tidal volume V_{tidal} must exceed the capacity of the empty pipe work and the collector when they are filled with air above the drainback level as well as the expansion of the fluid. An allowance for removal of air bubbles from pipes plus future slow leaks suggest an oversize of nominal 30 %.

$$V_{tidal} = 130\% \times (V_{Collector} + V_{expanded} + (V_{total} - V_{fluid}))$$

The vessel must be large enough to accommodate this swing in fluid content. Note that $V_{air} = V_{total} - V_{fluid}$

4. Calculation of pre-charge pressure

Unlike a fully filled system, a drainback system does not require an over-pressure to remove air from the top of the system. However, a slight over-pressure can be considered since the inlet pressure to a circulating pump must receive a pressure greater than 0.03 Bar at its inlet when cold to avoid cavitation. A standing water column in the drained-back status may achieve this. Care should be taken that a sealed drainback system does not become strongly sub-atmospheric after filling in particularly cold conditions, or from oxygen removal due to chemical reactions with metals. The latter process is capable of generating minus 0.2 Bar if the metals are unprotected. Once heated, the system pressure will rise and fulfil the pump's requirements. If oxygen has been removed, the gas in the system will be principally nitrogen and oxygen corrosion will cease.

Upon filling at 20°C, a $P_{initial}$ between zero and 0.5 Bar.

5.   Calculation of minimum air pocket to retain safety margin

Assume:

$P_{initial}$ $= 0.1$ Bar @ $20°C$.

P_{final} must not exceed 2.5 Bar

$V_{air\ cold}$ $= V_{total} - V_{fluid}$

$V_{air\ hot}$ $= V_{air\ cold} - V_{expanded}$ $= (V_{total} - V_{fluid}) - V_{expanded}$

$V_{expanded}$ $= 0.0153 \times V_{total}$

The ideal gas laws state that :

$(P1 \times V1) / T1 = (P2 \times V2) / T2$

Note T must be in Kelvin and atmospheric pressure assumed at 1 Bar.

Kelvin = Celsius + 273

Hence:

$(P_{initial} \times V_{air\ cold}) / (273 + 20)$ $= (P_{final} \times V_{air\ hot}) / (273 + 130)$

$((1.0 + 0.1) \times V_{air\ cold}) / 293$ $= ((1.0 + 2.5) \times V_{air\ hot}) / 403$

$1.1 / 293 \times V_{air\ cold}$ $= 3.5 / 403 \times V_{air\ hot}$

$V_{air\ cold} / V_{air\ hot}$ $= 3.5 / 403 \times 293 / 1.1$

$V_{air\ cold} / V_{air\ hot}$ $= 2.3$

$V_{air\ cold}$ $= 2.3 \times V_{air\ hot}$

Substituting from above:

$V_{total} - V_{fluid}$ $= 2.3 \times (V_{total} - V_{fluid} - 0.04 \times V_{total})$

V_{total} $= 2.3 \times (0.96 V_{total} - V_{fluid}) + V_{fluid}$

V_{total} $= 2.21 \times V_{total} - 1.3 V_{fluid}$

V_{fluid} $= 1.21 / 1.3 V_{total}$

V_{fluid} $= 0.931 \times V_{total}$

$V_{air\ cold}$ $=$ no less than 8% V_{total}

In practice, this value is increased for safety margin and an allowance for the action of the pump and hence becomes a guide to the minimum limit of air pocket size inside the drainback vessel.

Appendix F   Specimen commissioning sheet

For solar primary sealed systems – fully-filled and drainback. See Chapter 9 for further details.

1	User instructions explained and handed over	Yes/No
2	Decommission schedule for collector and cylinder left on site	Yes/No
3	Installation and maintenance instructions left on site	Yes/No
4	Specialist maintenance schedule (including frequency, maintenance and list of parts to be replaced during normal maintenance) left on site	Yes/No
5	Store commissioning certificate completed and signed	Yes/No
6	System drawing indicating hydraulic, valve and electrical connections	Yes/No
7	Conformity declarations for EU directives	Yes/No
8	All documentation to be kept visibly near store protected from heat, water and dust. Name of location where documentation is left	
9	Glazing format of solar collector	Tube/Flat
10	Absorber type	Selective/Non-selective
11	Net absorber or aperture area	m² Aperture/Absorber
12	Copy of EN 12975 conformity certificate left on site	Yes/No
13	Manufacturer's name of collector	
14	Unique serial no. of collector	
15	Maximum stagnation temperature of collector	°C
16	Maximum design pressure of collector	Bar
17	Maximum design pressure of pre-heat store exchanger	Bar
18	Maximum design pressure limit of system	Bar
19	System pressure setting when filled	Bar
20	Minimum allowable primary system pressure/level before user action required	Bar
21	Procedure for user to follow if primary pressure/level is below limit	
22	Location of primary system pressure gauge	
23	Frequency of regular test of pressure safety device	Monthly / Yearly / Biennially
24	Location of pressure safety device	
25	Location of electrical fused isolating switch	
26	Fuse rating	Amps
27	Electrical controls and temperature sensors operating correctly	Yes/No
28	Back-up DHW heating fitted with a thermostat responding to the solar pre-heat store	Yes/No
29	DHW thermostat setting	°C
30	Differential pump control setting	°C
31	Hysterisis setting about differential switching points	°C

32	Expansion or drainback vessel pre-charge	Bar
33	Expansion or drainback vessel capacity	Litres
34	Expansion capacity suitable to be hydraulically secure	Yes/No
35	Written warning left on site if there is potentially no automatic resumption of normal operation after stagnation	Yes/No/Not required
36	Lowest ambient temperature of primary system without freeze damage	°C
37	The heat transfer fluid provides freeze protection to	°C
38	Type of transfer fluid	Water or Water/Glycol
39	Corrosion inhibitor used	
40	Max. ambient temp for pump	°C
41	Min. ambient temperature for pump	°C
42	Circulation rate setting	Litres per minute
43	Noise at full circulation acceptable	Yes/No
44	Direction of circulation through collector and heat exchanger matched to sensor positions	Yes/No
45	If a drainback system, pipes fall greater than 1:33 or filled with antifreeze	Yes/No
46	Solar pre-heat store type	Combined with DHW / Separate from DHW
47	Solar primary heat exchanger type	Copper / Steel / Plain / Ribbed
48	Solar primary to secondary heat exchanger area	m²
49	Volume of dedicated solar pre-heat	litres
50	Location of DHW isolation valve	
51	Method of anti-scalding in DHW distribution	Pump control/TMV
52	Location of digital temperature gauge fitted to monitor risk of DHW overheating	
53	Limescale risk to heat exchanger	Low/Medium/High
54	Limescale control in heat exchanger	Cleaning hatch / Thermostat on primary circulation
55	Expected annual delivered solar energy to taps	kWh
56	Expected annual solar fraction of DHW	%
57	Method of performance calculation	SAP2005 / CIBSE Solar Design Guide / Other
58	Daily DHW load assumption	Litres per day at °C

Date of site visits for bacterial, water quality and access risk assessments	
Commissioned by	
Competent persons scheme unique identification number	
On behalf of	
Date system commissioned and handed over	
Signature of commissioning engineer	
Signature of user to confirm receipt and understanding (optional)	

Appendix G   Details of organisations from whom this guide is available

G1   Association of Plumbing and Heating Contractors

Unit 14
Ensign House
Ensign Business Centre
Westwood Way
Coventry
West Midlands
CV4 8JA

Tel: 024 7647 0626
Fax: 024 7647 0942
Website: www.aphc.co.uk

G2   Chartered Institution of Building Services Engineers

222 Balham High Road
Balham
London
SW12 9BS

Tel: 020 675 5211
Fax: 020 8675 5449
Website: www.cibse.org

G3   CORGI Services

1 Elmwood Chineham Business Park
Crockford Lane
Basingstoke
Hants
RG24 8WG

Tel: 01256 372200
Fax: 01256 708144
Website: www.trustcorgi.com

G4   Heating and Hotwater Industry Council

36 Holly Walk
Leamington Spa
Warwick
CV32 4LY

Tel: 0845 600 2200
Fax: 01926 423 284
Website: www.centralheating.co.uk

G5   Heating and Ventilating Contractors Association

ESCA House, 34 Palace Court
Bayswater
London
W2 4JG

Tel: 020 7313 4900
Fax: 020 7727 9268

Publications Department
Mansion House, Eamont Bridge
Penrith
Cumbria
CA10 2BX

Tel: 01768 860400
Fax: 01768 860401
Website: www.hvca.org.uk

G6   Institute of Domestic Heating & Environmental Engineers

Unit 35A
New Forest Enterprise Centre
Chapel Lane
Totton
Southampton
SO40 9LA

Tel: 023 8066 8900
Fax: 023 8066 0888
Website: www.idhee.org.uk